100 Bigfoot Nights
The Paranormal Link

By
Christine D. Parker

Vol. 3

BIGFOOT NIGHTS

100 Bigfoot Nights
The Paranormal Link
Vol. 3

Disclaimer – This is a true story. The names have been changed to protect the family and the neighborhood, due to the sensitive nature of this content.

Dedication

Dear Daddy

I love and miss you every day.
You were my strength and inspiration.
The world will never be the same.

Contents

Audio Recordings vii

Videos ix

Acknowledgments xi

1 Relentless Beast 1

2 The Rampage 5

3 Telling Tail.. 13

4 Where's Heidi? 21

5 Dark World... 29

6 The Phantom Act 35

7 The Creepy Crawler.. 43

8 Adam's Hauntings.. 51

9 The Hunting Club... 57

10 Final Warning 61

11 Out of Town Visitor... 67

12 The Faceless Beast 73

13 Primal Real Estate 83

14 Crypto Surveillance... 95

15 Fighting Destiny 101

16 Don't Go Upstairs 109

17 The Surrender... 117

18 Grim Reality 125

Audio Recordings

Audio recordings are available on our YouTube channel, 100BigfootNights and our website, 100BigfootNights.com

Sounds are listed by Chapter with "Book 3" in the title. We recommend using headphones when listening.

Chapter 1
Bang-Bang　　　　　　December 7, 2013　　11:45 p.m.
Chapter 2
Hitting raccoon?　　　December 10, 2013　4:20 a.m.
Vocal Yee's　　　　　　December 11, 2013　3:27 a.m.
Scream #3　　　　　　December 14, 2013　3:54 a.m.
Tantrum　　　　　　　December 18, 2013　11:58 p.m.
Chapter
Weird bird　　　　　　December 26, 2013　2:13 a.m.
Bizarre owl　　　　　　January 7, 2014　　5:34 a.m.
"Hey baby"　　　　　　January 23, 2014　　12:13 a.m.
Chapter 8
Screams and howls　　June 20, 2014　　　1:10 a.m.
Chapter 9
Birdcall?　　　　　　　August 7, 2014　　　5:37 a.m.
Chapter 12
Home alone　　　　　　November 15, 2014　5:29 p.m.
Chapter 13
I shall hurt them　　　Reverse Audio

Videos

Videos are available on our YouTube channel,
100BigfootNights and our website, 100BigfootNights.com
We recommended watching the videos on a computer.

Chapter 3
Strange lights   January 22, 2014   8:35 p.m.
Chapter 9
Bigfoot hunting   August 7, 2014   1:53 a.m.
Chapter 12
Faceless Beast   October 24, 2014 11:28 p.m.
Chapter 17
Moving camera   August 22, 2015   9:07 a.m.
Chapter 18
Ghost flash   November 16, 2015 10:03 p.m.
Bigfoot or Dog-man Peeking -added later for reference.

Acknowledgments

Dear husband, thank you for offering comfort when I need it the most. Together we have faced many challenges, some terrifying and others devastatingly heartbreaking. I could have never finished the book series without you, and I love that you are always optimistic.

Thank you to our sons; you are amazing men and always working together to tackle the challenges we face as a family. United, we stand against all things sent to destroy us.

Dear brother Edmund and his family, thank you for all your love and support. Your strength helped us all survive the most painful time of our lives. I rely on your strength and courage daily and await your encouraging phone calls.

Dear sister Antoinette and her wonderful husband, Mike, and family, your love and support give us hope and keep us looking forward. Your kind and generous family reminds us that we can get through our worst times together.

I would also like to thank my mother, who makes me proud. She, too, has gone through many struggles and survived. She epitomizes a strong, determined woman with a genuine love of family. To my stepfather, thank you for understanding and offering love and support. It was a pleasure spending time with you.

Dear Aunt Gloria, thank you for your advice, love, and prayers. We appreciate all your inspirational connections.

Dear Uncle Danny, thank you for always thinking of us. Your love and thoughtfulness comforted many during our time of need. We appreciate what you did very much.

Dear cousin Christine and her wonderful husband, Joe, and family, thank you for helping and welcoming us with open arms. Your understanding, love, courage, and support give us the strength to face challenges. You are an inspiration to us all.

Dear Aunt Helen and family, thank you for your love and support. You make the most difficult times bearable. Your loving and caring family is a true blessing, and your courage is inspiring. We are forever grateful to all of you.

Dear cousin Arnold, and his beautiful wife, Sharon, thank you for the gift of memories. It's the good memories that give us comfort. We appreciate all the love and support. Thanks for keeping us in your thoughts.

Thanks again to Tal H. Branco for all his advice and wisdom.

To Mr. Oxley, the book cover designer, thank you for your kind words of encouragement and another outstanding unique piece of art. It was a pleasure to work with such a professional again. Your ideas are genius, and your art is reflective.

To Astrid, thank you for helping to edit the book.

To the fans of my book series, thank you for your kind words and support. It meant so much to us when we felt all alone. We stood with all of you, facing the battle for truth no matter how dark the path. I want you to know we discovered it together, and I thank you for allowing us to tell our story and encouraging others to do so.

100 Bigfoot Nights
The Paranormal Link

1
Relentless Beast

Tree with protruding sharp stick (enlarged lower right)

Maybe we were part of "their clan." According to Mr. Hill, this was possible due to our unpleasant interactions with the creatures. If so, I thought it was definitely the unwelcome part. He also suspected the beasts would not even try hiding from us anymore.

I could only imagine what he meant because they had already shown themselves several times. I kept picturing opening the French door curtains and seeing a beastly face looking back. It was terrifying just thinking about it. I told myself; *just don't look out the French door windows at night.* Problem solved. I wished all our problems were as simple, but unfortunately, that wasn't the case.

We had Bigfoot drinking out of our pool and trying to sneak into our house, and I thought listening to them was bad enough. Their talking, hollering, branch breaking, knocking, mimicking, and throwing things had become somewhat expected. Now, I consider those things the good ole' days.

Obviously, Bigfoot trying to sneak into the house was a much bigger problem. It was horrifying, considering we didn't know what it wanted. Was the Bigfoot looking for food, as Mr. Hill suggested, or did it want something else?

No one knew the answer, especially us, since these creatures didn't behave as we expected. Everything we did to keep them away had backfired. We set up cameras, shot the yard with flashlights, and brandished guns. We thought we sent a clear signal that we didn't want them anywhere near the house. We chased them away every time they came close, and even the dogs barked at them. But apparently, it had produced the opposite results.

We acknowledged their presence and interacted with them by responding to their actions. We were giving them attention. It reminded me of an old saying, "Any attention given, whether good or bad, is still attention."

We were facing a new aspect of terror because of our actions. Not knowing what would happen next, I called Mr. Hill again. He still thought the Bigfoot was just looking for food, but as we talked, it became evident that we had another problem.

Mr. Hill was very interested when I mentioned the strange damage we found in the house when we bought it. He asked many questions, and as I explained some of the damage we found, he kept saying, "Oh no, oh no."

Knowing it could only be bad news, I finally asked Mr. Hill what he thought. He said the damage reminded him of something he had read about concerning the creatures, but he would not elaborate. He would call me back after doing some research. After we hung up, I dreaded his return phone call. I didn't tell him then, but the terrifying thought of the creatures in the house before we bought it had already crossed my mind. I just didn't want to think about it. It was all too horrifying and the last thing I wanted to know.

I was busy speculating why a Bigfoot would try to sneak into our house. There had to be a reason. Why didn't it just break the door down and walk in? I tried to look at it from a logical perspective.

The night the creature attempted to sneak into the house, it knew we were awake inside. Dean and I were just outside, taking pictures of its footprints by the swimming pool. It was probably watching us the whole time. In fact, we were all home, including our four dogs. Why would a Bigfoot want to contend with all of us for a simple meal?

I couldn't help but wonder what did the creature want? What would have happened? *Had the deadbolt been unlocked, and I stayed in the family room with Dean and the dogs?* The Bigfoot would have quietly snuck into the house, and depending on which way it went inside, it could have easily made it to the kitchen before the dogs reacted. Our four dogs would have barely slowed the creature down. It also could have snuck upstairs if it had gone in another direction. In that case, we wouldn't have even known it was in the house until it was too late. What were the creature's intentions?

Knowing that a Bigfoot could easily break through the doors and windows only added to the mystery. Until I remembered something Mr. Hill said about Bigfoot; "They feared guns. The creatures were aware of the damage a gun could do; even a grazing shot could be deadly to them due to infection."

If true, sneaking in from the creature's perspective would make sense. We even recorded what could have been Bigfoot sneaking up to the house and whispering the words *"Bang-bang."* Did they know what these words meant?

Dean and the boys were armed, and Bigfoot knew this from watching us. I, too, had a loaded gun nearby after this particularly horrifying incident. Dean had given me his 357 Magnum. I had shot the Magnum before, and it was easy to operate. I kept the weapon within arm's reach. He placed his Colt 45 in the desk drawer next to him, along with additional clips. Of course, I had hoped we would never have to use them, but having them may have prevented a catastrophic event.

I think the creatures breaking the doors down or busting through the windows would definitely be their worst and last option. Although it was always an option, depending on how motivated and angry the creature could become. Since we were dealing with an army of them, I assumed it was only one or two causing all the problems. It seemed more likely than not. Logically, we would have been dead by now if they all wanted us dead. Therefore, what were we up against?

Was it beastly curiosity, anger, hunger, or retaliation? What did the creature want? Unfortunately, despite my speculation, we didn't have any answers. The truth is, nobody did. As Dean pointed out, "How do you get into the mind of a creature?"

Audio Book 3 Chapter 1

2
The Rampage

Camera focused on mailbox

Dean moved the night vision camera in the pool area. He put the camera on the fence to the left of the French doors and then angled it to view the back of them. Then Dean turned off the porch light; as if to dare the Bigfoot that turned the door handle to approach. At night, he watched that camera, anxiously awaiting the creature's return.

However, the Bigfoot return was the last thing I wanted. I wanted the camera to keep them away. The cameras usually worked to deter the creatures unless they suddenly became photogenic overnight. Either way, I tried to avoid the French doors after dark. I knew the camera only covered the backside of them and part of the porch. Therefore, several Bigfoot could have been in the pool beyond the camera's view, and we would not have seen them.

Although I thought, let them have the pool, we wouldn't defend it. No more responding to the creatures by chasing them with guns and flashlights. I figured protecting the house was more important. After dark, we would keep the dogs inside as much as possible. I was terrified of ever seeing the door handle move again. The incident was disturbing, but we had to move forward as usual.

~~~

With Christmas just around the corner and decorations on the front porch in boxes, we had to decide how to decorate the front yard. We didn't want to draw more unwanted attention to our house. Mr. Hill had told us that the creatures liked shiny things. So Dean placed a colorful, shiny wreath on the mailbox near the street to draw attention away. He also put a few less shiny decorations on the front porch and nothing on the front lawn. Sadly, we agreed not to set up our main display, the reindeer and sleigh.

When our children were younger, I built the sleigh and reindeer out of wood. The first reindeer I made was Rudolph, with his red nose. I made several reindeer, jig-sawing each and hand-painting them. It was more than just a display; it was precious memories of our children and the neighborhood kids who used to play in it. It brought so much joy since it was large enough for them to sit in and pretend.

Dean pointed out that it would be the first time it wasn't set up on the front lawn in nineteen years. It was the end of a family tradition. He packed it up and took it back to storage.

He said, "When we get out of here, we can set it back up again."

It was the best we could do considering our situation.

~~~

After setting up the few decorations the following night, we heard banging close to the house. It sounded like someone with hands pounding a rock against something, trying to open it. It was loud, annoying, and consistent, with short pauses in-between. I guess it could have been a muscular raccoon that found something, but I didn't think so. The raccoons were usually very vocal, and they fought over everything.

The banging could have been a young Bigfoot that found something worth opening. Listening to it, I thought, *whatever you are, just stay away from the house; you can do whatever you want, just stay away.* Despite the constant banging at 3:00 a.m., we decided not to respond. Whatever was banging the rock didn't appear on the cameras or near the doors. I was relieved when the banging finally stopped.

At the time, we had four-night vision cameras, three televisions in the office that displayed them, and a broken monitor we kept for audio since the microphone still worked.

Two of our night vision cameras were viewed through one television screen, the camera over the top of the garage and the camera viewing the back of the French doors. We could only view one camera at a time by manually switching the input on the television. We mostly viewed the camera focused on the French doors all night.

The second television screen displayed the long-range night vision camera installed on the front porch. It viewed a large section of the front of the house and to the right of the mailbox.

The third television screen displayed the night vision camera, usually positioned to view across the front porch. However, Dean repositioned it during Christmas to view the front of the house and the mailbox. (See chapter photo). Dean said after Christmas, he would move the camera to view across the front porch again. We constantly moved and replaced the cameras if they broke.

Over the next few nights, we heard what sounded like a ***Bigfoot hitting a raccoon***, more animal ***screams,*** sneaking around sounds, and a few vocal ***yees.*** Most of these sounds we had heard before and figured they would continue, especially since we weren't responding to them.

~~~

On December 18, the creatures were in the forest. I spent the day trying to capture a video of them, but the forest was too dense. It was a waste of time, and I was disappointed after watching my videos. I should have spent the day shopping for Christmas. It was a week away, and I still needed more presents.

Later that evening, at 7:30 p.m., Adam called to let us know he was almost home. Dean switched the television screen to view the camera over the garage, so we could watch Adam exit his truck safely. He also met Adam on the front porch. After they entered the house, Adam came into the office to talk to us. He wanted to discuss his relationship with his girlfriend, Amanda. He told us that they had broken up earlier that day. They were having problems and it seemed they broke up at least once a week. Dean and I had not seen Amanda since the night she saw the Bigfoot watching her from the forest. We didn't want to tell Adam, but we figured the incident only hastened their relationship's end. Dean and I knew we would never see Amanda again.

Adam had bought Amanda a heart-shaped ruby ring for Christmas. He wanted to know if he should give it to her. He tried explaining the importance of the ring, but it was apparent he was holding something back that he didn't want us to know. We told him to do whatever he thought was best. Adam said, "I bought the ring for her, and I wouldn't feel right giving it to someone else. I think she should have it," as he bowed his head in sadness.

Dean and I agreed, even though Adam figured it would be the last time he saw her. We talked for a few more hours, trying to comfort him. When we finished talking, Adam left the room to go upstairs, but before he went up the staircase, he paused at the bottom and said, "By the way, the creatures are here tonight. The hairs on the back of my neck stood up when I got out of my truck."

I replied, "I know; I've been trying to video them all day."

Dean followed Adam to the staircase and patted him on the shoulder, while on his way to the kitchen to get us some more coffee. When Dean returned we discussed Adam and Amanda's situation. We were very sad. Adam was going through a lot, and all we could do was listen. It was a helpless feeling.

Soon we were on our computers again and listening to the monitor. Outside it was peaceful and quiet.

All our sons were upstairs, and all the dogs were sleeping. Cockapoo was under the desk, Foxy was on the carpet behind me, Rocky was on the couch, and Heidi was lying on the dining room floor.

A little before midnight, Dean was listening to the news on his computer. He heard an interesting story and wanted to tell me about it. He took off his headphones, and I stopped what I was doing to listen. We talked for a few minutes when suddenly, we heard hollering. Something yelled out in a bizarre tone a few times and then stopped. It was shocking as it resonated from the monitor's speaker. Immediately, *I thought*, Bigfoot.

Dean and I inquisitively looked at each other and then at the cameras. I jumped up to check the recording device by the monitor. I recalled earlier that we had turned it off when we talked to Adam. I turned it on as Dean opened his desk drawer, pulled out his pistol, and chambered a round. He turned his chair to watch the cameras.

I sat at my desk and unzipped the bag with my pistol in it. I placed the pistol on the desk in front of me. We didn't say a word as we stared at the cameras and waited.

The yelling started again, except this time, it was louder. The sound resonated between our home, the street, and the forest. The yelling was so loud that we couldn't tell which direction the creature was traveling, although I hoped it was moving away from our house.

After a few agonizing minutes of listening to the Bigfoot, I began to panic. The yelling was becoming louder and more intense. The beast was heading towards us. I cringed.

Dean stood up and came around the desk with his pistol. He positioned himself to watch the doors, the windows, and the cameras as he stood behind me. Terrified, I was afraid to move or make a sound. My heart was pounding so fast that I could hardly breathe or swallow. The wailing, creepy tone was unlike any sound I had ever heard, although the intense volume was distinctive. It was a Bigfoot, but worst of all, it sounded extremely upset.

When I could finally move, I anxiously picked up my gun and stood beside Dean. He noticed I wasn't breathing right, so he leaned over and whispered, "We have to stop meeting like this."

I half-smiled and took a breath. I just wanted it to stop, but it didn't. Something horrifying was happening outside our front door, and we had no idea what to expect. It was like all hell broke loose, and we were standing in the middle of it. Maybe we were listening to a creature's territorial dispute or cries of pain and despair. Either way, I felt like an unwilling witness and didn't want to hear it. Also, we were recording these hellish sounds, and maybe they weren't meant to be recorded.

Dean whispered again, "Honey, I got this; everything is going to be okay."

I wanted to believe him, but it sure didn't feel okay. That beast was hollering, and it was loud and fast. One second it sounded close, and the other, it seemed blocks away. *How was it doing that?* Why didn't we see the beast on the cameras when at times, it sounded like it was in front of the house? It was circling somewhere in the darkness, going back and forth.

We both knew to stay away from the doors and windows. We didn't even have to talk about it. Listening to a creature on a rampage was incredibly intense. They were unbelievable sounds of a beast that didn't belong in a neighborhood. Where families were sleeping or driving home for the night, it was a potentially dangerous situation. I felt sorry for anyone unfortunate enough to be outside and cross its path. *I thought* no creature yelling like that was afraid of being seen or heard. The beast was having a tantrum, and nothing was going to stop it.

It also didn't sound like it was moving through the forest. It sounded like it was walking up and down the middle of the street. It continued pacing and hollering through the neighborhood, and there were tense moments where I felt like a sitting duck. Waiting, watching, and praying that nothing more terrifying would happen.

Although Dean seemed ready for it, he appeared calm. I don't know how he did it, but having him beside me was reassuring. He also loaded a rifle and placed it within arm's reach.

The beast went on for several minutes; it kept hollering and hollering when suddenly, it occurred to me that our dogs were not barking. Usually, when they heard a strange sound, they would respond by barking out of control and running to the French doors to get out. *Where were they?* I quickly looked for the dogs, but to my surprise, they were gone. There wasn't a dog in sight. Evidently, their instincts told them to hide. I wanted to do the same thing but felt there was nowhere to run from this screaming beast. We had no choice but to face it, and just when I thought things couldn't get any worse, they did.

In the distance, we heard an abrupt yell in a gargled, barking tone. Due to the volume of it, I immediately thought it was another Bigfoot. Although it sounded a few blocks away, the abrupt creature was responding to the other's beckoning cries. Another Bigfoot was the last thing I wanted to hear, as it abruptly yelled a few times.

My heart jumped again, but to our surprise and relief, the hollering beast near us began to move away. Its blood-curdling screams were fading into the distance. It was over for us, but not for the neighborhood. Its hollering rampage echoed for blocks. *(Tantrum)*

Dean took the gun from my sweaty hands and put it away. He also cleared his weapon and placed it on the desk. I sat down and rubbed my face. I nervously stated, "Well, I guess there was no way for us to ignore that."

He said, "I told you everything was going to be okay," as he leaned over and hugged me.

I replied, "What the hell was that all about? And did you notice the dogs left? They were gone!"

"Yes," he said, "That only proves they're smarter than us."

We talked about what happened for the rest of the night. It was a long and stressful night again.

How many stressful nights had it been? I thought. How many nights awake, protecting the house, listening for the creatures? Out of curiosity, I went online and calculated the days; it came out to four hundred and thirty-two stressful nights and counting. *Will this ever end?*

~~~

Later, when I sent a copy of the audio recording to Mr. Hill, he confirmed it was a Bigfoot. He stated there were two of them. Apparently, there were other documented recordings similar to these types of vocals. He said, "I listened very carefully to the recording, and in between the hollering, there are subtle sounds they make. I was listening for them; sure enough, all parts of the recording indicated Bigfoot. Most people are unaware of the subtle sounds we listen for on the recordings."

Bigfoot investigators listened for subtle sounds? I found this interesting because the volume's tone and magnitude seemed most important to me.

He then asked, "What happened that night? Something must have happened for it to be wailing like that."

I replied, "We don't know. To us, everything outside seemed normal and creepy, as usual."

Audio Book 3 Chapter 2

3
Telling Tail

Rocky waiting for his Christmas stocking

A week later, on the night of Christmas Eve, Rocky was sitting by the fireplace in the dining room, waiting for his stocking. His tongue was hanging out of his mouth, anticipating his tasty treats. Foxy, Heidi, and Cockapoo quietly waited for the boys to come downstairs to the dining room. Minutes later, when the boys arrived, it was officially Christmas.

William took Foxy's stocking down from the fireplace mantel. He sat on the floor to feed her gently. Jack was feeding Rocky and Heidi, and they were playing. He tossed their treats up in the air so they could catch them. Adam was feeding Cockapoo her treats, and, in between her gobbling them, she was barking and growling at Rocky and Heidi for misbehaving.

It was complete chaos and a true blessing in the middle of the night. As I stood there watching them, I couldn't help but think how lucky I was despite everything. We were all together, and Foxy survived to enjoy another Christmas; that's what really mattered.

Next, it was time to open presents, and by 12:30 a.m., we were finished. While everyone gathered their gifts and took time to enjoy them, Dean went into the kitchen to make breakfast for dinner. We called it "brinner." It was one of our favorite meals, and soon, he had every burner on the stove going. Dean was the main cook in the family. He was frying peppered bacon and maple sausage, cooking fresh-cut potatoes, and preparing his special dish, feta and eggs. The toaster was popping out four toasted pieces of bread at a time. I offered to butter them while managing to stay out of Dean's way.

Next to me, William was making pots of coffee, each one being a different blend. He had received a variety of coffees for Christmas. He and Dean couldn't wait to try them. When I finished the toast, I sat at the kitchen island to watch Dean cook. He had the stove exhaust on to vent out the different aromas.

I commented on how good it smelled. I was basking in the smells when suddenly, it dawned on me. All those smells were venting outside into the backyard behind the stove. I looked at Dean and said, "Oh no! Do you realize we are the only family in our housing area with a vented stove? When we remodeled the kitchen, we put in the gas line."

"I know, I have the fans on," he said.

"No, that's not what I meant. Our gas stove has an exhaust

fan. We cut a hole in the wall behind the stove."

"Yes, so?" he replied while turning the bacon.

"Everyone else has electric stoves with no outside vents," I stated.

Dean gave me a nonchalant look.

"The Bigfoot can smell what you're cooking. They can smell the bacon," I said.

"Okay?" He muttered.

"You're always cooking bacon when we eat breakfast in the middle of the night; the smell of the bacon is probably what's attracting them. They love bacon!" I stated.

"Who told you that?" He asked.

"I saw it once on a television show. They were cooking bacon to attract a Bigfoot," I replied.

"Oh c'mon, everybody loves bacon!" Adam yelled from the dining room after overhearing our conversation.

William also commented, "You could probably smell that bacon for a mile."

Jack walked through the kitchen and said, "There's probably a Bigfoot right now standing behind that wall (in the backyard) gettin a whiff of that smell."

"Thanks, Jack, that sure makes me feel a lot better," I stated sarcastically.

"Well, what are you going to do? You can't stop cooking bacon or anything else," He replied.

Unfortunately, Jack was right. He summed up our entire situation; what could we do about anything? I moved away from the wall to the other side of the island. I had the chills just thinking about it. They were making light of my observation, but to me, it seemed relevant. Because a few days before Christmas, Rocky was watching something in the backyard, and I had the feeling it was a Bigfoot...

It happened early in the evening; Jack had let Rocky outside in the pool area. I told Jack I would watch Rocky, so he could go back upstairs. I was sitting in the office watching him on the camera. Rocky was standing just outside the French doors sniffing the porch. A few minutes later, he ran across the porch to the chain-link gate and started barking. We have a four-foot chain-link fence with a gate that separates the side-pool yard from our backyard.

Rocky stood a few feet from the gate, barking at something he was watching in our backyard. His hackles were up, and he seemed upset, but his tail was wagging. It was wagging as if he recognized what he was watching. It was very strange. I could clearly see Rocky on the camera, but I couldn't see what he was barking at; we didn't have a camera viewing the backyard.

Rocky barked and barked, suddenly stopped, and then glanced behind him as if he heard something in that direction. He quickly looked back into the yard, barked one more time, and then ran to the French doors to get into the house. I also ran to the French doors to get him inside. After he came in, I closed the door, locked it, and ran into the kitchen to tell Dean something was in the backyard. He was in the middle of making dinner, so by the time he checked the yard, nothing was there.

Rocky's behavior was very strange. Even though I couldn't see what he was barking at in either direction, his head was tilted upward.

Although I couldn't blame our sons for making light of my observation, I never told them what happened with Rocky. Suddenly Dean announced it was time to eat as he pulled dinner plates from the cupboard. We filled our plates and thanked him for "brinner." It was delicious, to say the least.

After we finished eating, we all decided to watch a movie. It was a nice change from watching cameras all night. I told Dean, "I could get used to this," as I closed my eyes and fell asleep on the couch before the movie's end.

Dean and our sons stayed up the rest of the night drinking coffee and playing with electronic gadgets they got for Christmas.

~~~

The following night we heard a *(weird bird)* at 2:13 a.m., and then on January 7, a *(bizarre owl)*. Both of these sounds seemed unusual due to the tone and pattern. Although we have owls in the neighborhood, a few days later, while standing in the backyard, Jack spotted one sitting in our neighbor's tree. When Jack told me about the owl, I felt a sense of relief. I thought, maybe that's what Rocky was watching in the backyard the night he tilted his head upward and barked. He was watching an owl. It seemed logical, and I was more than willing to believe it until Rocky started doing something else that bothered me.

During the night, Rocky started standing behind the curtains of the French doors, peeking through the windowpanes, barking, and wagging his tail. Sometimes he would scratch at the door wanting to go outside. It kept happening every few nights, and it was scary because he wagged his tail as if he was happy to see someone or something.

The first few times he did it, Dean turned on the porch light and looked out the French doors but saw nothing. We also didn't see anything on the camera. We discussed Rocky's strange behavior, and Dean thought maybe he was watching his reflection in the windowpanes, and that's why his tail was wagging. It sounded like a plausible answer, but Rocky had never done it before. It gave me the creeps, and again, I assumed he was watching something else. It happened a few more times.

~~~

Early in the evening on January 22, I saw strange lights flickering in the forest. Months ago, I promised Jack that if I saw any more lights, I would record them, so I did. The lights appeared strange because of the height and the way they moved. They were definitely not fireflies or eye shine. They flickered a few times and then disappeared. *(Strange lights)*

After dinner, Dean came into the office, and I showed him the video of the lights. He agreed they were strange and that Jack would be interested in them. He sat at his computer and me at mine as we talked about other strange things happening to Adam.

Adam was working long hours and coming home late. He had called us a few times to tell us there were strange noises inside his work building. The noises were strange because Adam worked alone at night, and we believed the building was haunted. Dean and I discussed it, and all the signs pointed in that direction.

Nevertheless, we worried about him. Dean called Adam to ask if he was okay and when he expected to be home. Adam said he was fine and would be home by ten. By 10 p.m., he was home safely, and the house was locked tight.

Another long night was ahead for Dean and me, and it was time for a few cups of coffee. Dean always drinks coffee during the night. I also drink some coffee but mostly prefer diet soda or "special tea." It's a sugar-free tea with lemon that Dean buys at the local all-night gas station. He also sometimes surprises me with my favorite snack - a small apple pie. He says he loves to see me smile, and that night he surprised me. I ate a small apple pie, minus Rocky's piece.

Cockapoo was sleeping in her little bed under the desk, where she usually lays. Foxy was lying on the floor next to me on a soft carpet. Rocky was sleeping on the couch, and Heidi was upstairs with the boys. Outside, it seemed quiet, but due to the static on the monitor, we didn't always hear the creatures approaching.

At 12:13 a.m., Rocky jumped up from a sound sleep. He barked and growled, looked at the French doors, and then charged toward them. What he did was startling, but he had done it a few times before. We looked at the camera viewing outside the French doors but didn't see anything. Rocky barked a few more times and then quietly pressed his nose against the window behind the curtains. His tail was wagging out of control.

Cockapoo and Foxy also woke up, but they didn't bark. They were quietly listening. Rocky stood under the curtains wagging his tail for a few more minutes. I watched him until he finally returned to the office, jumped on the couch, and went back to sleep as if nothing had happened. Dean went back to playing his game on the computer.

I looked at Rocky and told Dean, "I swear he's watching something."

Dean couldn't see Rocky in the window from his side of the desk. I said, "His tail is wagging like when he sees someone he knows, and he must have heard something."

"I don't know," he replied. "Every time I look outside, there's nothing there."

"Something is there," I insisted. "We just don't see it. Maybe Rocky sees a Bigfoot he recognizes, and it's calling him. We don't let him out in the middle of the night anymore. Remember when Mr. Hill said, 'They have decided to let you see them?' Well, maybe 'they' have changed their minds. What do you think?" I asked.

"I think it just keeps getting stranger and stranger," he said as he continued playing his game on the computer.

I sat on the couch next to Rocky. He woke up, and I petted his head. He looked me in the eyes, and I asked him what he saw as if he would answer. Rocky seemed so sad, and it was a mystery until a few days later, when I listened to the audio recording from that night.

On the recording, I heard Rocky when he started barking at the French doors, and then I heard a faint voice. It said, *(Hey baby)* and then growled at him. It was creepy and horrifying. I played it again and recalled all the times Rocky looked out the window. He was watching them, and they were calling him by his nickname. Our sons always say, "Hey baby," to Rocky, and so do I.

I knew something was wrong. The creatures were calling Rocky, but why? Why did they focus on him? I felt he was in grave danger, and we needed to watch him better when he went outside. Although I also had the feeling, after watching Rocky in the yard barking by the chain-link gate, that he too was beginning to understand the danger.

I thought about the night Rocky barked through the chain link gate, looked behind him, and then ran into the house. He was anxiously afraid; that's why watching him bothered me so much. Sometimes when we call him, and he doesn't want to obey, he barks and wags his tail, but his hackles aren't raised with us.

It also bothered me that Rocky could see them, but Dean couldn't. Why? I should have asked Mr. Hill what he meant when he said, "They have decided to let you see them."

Dean was right things were becoming stranger. There was something not right about the Bigfoot, which also bothered me, but I couldn't figure it out.

When Dean heard the audio recording, he was upset. He made it perfectly clear that every time Rocky looked out the window, he would turn on the extra lighting and shine a flashlight into the yard. He intended to stop the creatures calling Rocky, and I urgently agreed.

Audio Book 3 Chapter 3
Video Strange lights

4
Where's Heidi?

Footprints by the pool again

On January 31, Dean and I were in the office. He was looking up stuff on the computer, and I was writing while trying to listen to a recording. It was late afternoon.

Jack was playing in the pool area with Rocky and Heidi. Jack and Heidi were chasing Rocky, and he was playfully barking and growling at them. They were also running in and out of the house. The left side door of the French door was cracked open. Under the desk, Cockapoo was also whimpering and barking every time they went in and out. I kept telling Jack to stop and close the door. The open door made me nervous, and the noise was very distracting, to say the least.

Jack pulled the curtains over the French doors. I guess he figured the open door was the problem. Therefore, I would quit complaining if I couldn't see it was open. Amazingly, his idea worked, and I thought the door was closed. It made me feel more comfortable, and with my headphones on, I could ignore them and concentrate on writing. I guess Jack used his degree in psychology to trick me.

When I finished listening to the recording, I worked for a while longer when suddenly; it occurred to me that it was quiet. I looked at the cameras and saw it was getting dark. Worried about Jack and the dogs, I went to look for them. Behind the closed French door curtains, the door was open, and when I looked into the yard, I saw no sign of Jack or the dogs. The only obvious thing I noticed was large, wet-looking footprints beside the swimming pool.

Shocked, I slammed the door, locked it and yelled, "Where's Jack and the dogs?!"

As I ran to ask Dean in the office, "Did you notice if they came into the house?!"

He said, "Yes, I think they came in a while ago. I heard a noise in the kitchen."

"Are you sure?! I said.

"Yes, what's the problem?" He asked.

Frantic, I replied, "The French door was open! And there are large wet-looking footprints next to the pool again! Where are they?!"

I ran through the office and to the family room, yelling for Jack and the dogs. They weren't in the family room, so I ran up the back stairs while Dean went up the front staircase. We both needed to know if they were okay and if they were the ones in the pool.

When I reached the top of the stairs, I heard Dean yelling, "I found Rocky and Heidi!"

They were safe in our bedroom, hiding under the bed. I yelled back, "I hear Jack's shower on; he's taking a shower!"

He was also safely inside the house. I banged on the bathroom door and yelled, "Jack!"

"What?!" He yelled back.

"When you were outside playing with the dogs, did you or the dogs go in the pool?!" I asked.

"No!" He abruptly replied.

Dean came through the spare bedroom and into the back hallway with the dogs. He stood beside me and said, "The dogs are dry."

I yelled to Jack through the bathroom door again, "What time did you come back into the house?!"

"I'm taking a shower!" He said.

"Just answer my question!" I pleaded, "It's important!"

Jack turned the shower off so we could quit yelling and calmly asked from the other side of the door, "What's wrong?"

I quickly explained and asked about the footprints.

He replied, "There were no footprints around the pool when I came back in about ten minutes ago. I left the door open because the dogs were still out. I figured you'd close the door and lock it when the dogs came back in."

I took a deep breath, leaned my head against the bathroom door, and replied, "We didn't see them or know the door was open behind the curtains. You should have told us when you came back inside."

"I thought you knew, I was in the kitchen," Jack replied.

Dean said, "I'm going to check the pool area," as he quickly headed downstairs.

The dogs and I followed him. When we reached the office, Dean grabbed his gun while I snatched the camera and an envelope. I needed an envelope next to the footprints for a size comparison. Mr. Hill had advised us to do this if we ever photographed footprints again.

We kept the dogs inside while we went outside. The dogs were barking and clawing at the French doors making lots of noise. Darkness was falling, and seeing the footprints around the pool again gave me the chills. How could this have happened? A Bigfoot was outside in the pool before nightfall. I looked at the fence, and then, it dawned on me we had provided the means for the Bigfoot to stay hidden. When we bought the house, we put in the six-foot wooden privacy fence to secure the pool. The fence provided cover for the creatures by hiding them from the street view. It was impossible for anyone to see them as they drove by.

Dean stood guard while I photographed the footprints. The footprints began at the pool steps and traveled about thirty feet along the left side of the pool. They tapered off and ended at the lawn on the far side of the yard, where we assumed the creature exited by jumping over the fence. Over the fence on the corner was a patch of trees and then the street, followed by the forest.

~~~

After photographing the prints, we returned to the office to look at them on the computer. Dean and I agreed that the size of the footprints indicated it was a large creature. Dean estimated the creature's foot was between fifteen to sixteen inches long and at least five inches wide.

We were shocked that this had happened in broad daylight with us home in the office only a few feet away. As I sat at the computer staring at the photos, the horrifying reality of the incident began to emerge.

A Bigfoot was in the pool area just outside the French doors, and they were open. The creature could have easily entered the house, but it didn't. Dean and I were twenty feet from the door, yet the beast chose to leave us alone, but what about Jack? The Bigfoot must have been watching him and the dogs playing in the yard. How did the Bigfoot know Jack wasn't going outside again after he came in the house? Jack was going in and out all afternoon. Even we didn't know.

The bold creature entered the pool despite Jack, the dogs, and the open door. Maybe it was thirsty, but it could have found water somewhere else. It seemed like a deliberate act, and if Jack had surprised the creature, this would have been a different story.

What this creature did was disturbing. It was also upsetting thinking about what could have happened to Rocky and Heidi. After all, they were hiding under our bed when Dean found them. Maybe they were already inside or ran inside after confronting the beast. I guess they could have barked and growled at the creature before they ran, but we wouldn't have noticed. Again, we thought

Jack was outside playing with them.

We also ignored Cockapoo's whimpering and barking in the office due to Jack playing with Rocky and Heidi. Rocky and Heidi playing in the house always upset Cockapoo; she disapproved of them misbehaving.

Thinking about what could have happened made me sick. I started to rub my stomach when Dean noticed and asked if I was okay. I told him I felt ill and needed to go lie down. He reassured me nothing bad had happened. He said, "Jack and the dogs are fine and all the doors are locked. I'll keep an eye on things, you go lay down."

A few minutes later, I was lying on the couch in the family room when Jack came downstairs and asked about the footprints. I explained, and he said that just before he went into the house, he heard loud crackling sounds coming from the forest as if someone were stepping through the dry foliage. It was loud enough that Jack stood on a chair by the pool to look over the fence but didn't see anything. He said, "I looked at the forest, and the sounds stopped. Then I came back inside to take a shower."

I told him, "Well at least we know where it came from. It was watching you but I can't figure out how it knew you weren't going outside again. Assuming it didn't want a confrontation, it must have known somehow. Aside from what happened, that's what else bothers me about the creatures - they seem to know things they shouldn't."

Trying to stay one step ahead of the Bigfoot was tiring and draining. We couldn't figure out what to expect next. It felt as if we somehow always managed to avoid a catastrophic event. Was it due to divine intervention or strictly coincidence? *Who knows?*

~~~

On February 19, at 9:30 a.m., Dean and I had just finished breakfast. We were in the family room watching television, winding down from our nightly surveillance. We had nothing planned all morning, and I was getting comfortable on the couch, ready to fall asleep.

Dean was sitting in the chair next to me, also dozing off, but the weight of his head dropping kept waking him up. He looked so tired and beat; I guess I looked the same. As my heavy eyes began to fall, I took one last look at Dean and told him to go to bed. He needed to get some sleep. I offered to stay downstairs and take care of the dogs in case they needed to go outside. Dean agreed and headed off to bed.

Three of our dogs, Rocky, Foxy, and Cockapoo, were already asleep, lying on the floor next to the couches. I assumed Heidi was behind me, sleeping on the chair. The house inside was very quiet. Jack was asleep upstairs, but William and Adam were gone. I closed my eyes and quickly fell asleep.

The next thing I remembered was waking up to the dogs bellowing. Cockapoo was wailing in a screeching tone, Foxy was barking, and Rocky was whimpering and barking. I didn't move or open my eyes. I was so exhausted the last thing I wanted to do was get up. I just listened to them, hoping all the excitement was due to Jack coming downstairs. The dogs loved to see Jack in the morning. He gave treats and played with them.

When I didn't hear Jack's voice, and Rocky started licking my face and whimpering, I opened one eye to see them. I saw Rocky standing before me, Foxy barking while lying on the floor, and Cockapoo standing next to her, still screaming. Believing they were fine and still not wanting to get up, I told them to calm down and go back to sleep as I rolled over to prevent Rocky from licking my face.

All the dogs went quiet for a second, and that's when I heard what I thought was Heidi clawing at the backdoor, trying to open it. She and Foxy could open the doors by putting their claws in the crack between the door and the frame and then pulling. Of course, the door had to be opened a crack for them to get out, but they always tried, and that's the sound I heard.

I assumed it was Heidi because all the other dogs were beside me. I was just about to get up and open the backdoor to let Heidi out when the clawing stopped, and I heard a dog running up the back staircase. A few seconds later, the clawing started again, but this time I heard clawing at the French doors on the other side of the house. I figured Heidi had run up the back staircase and then gone down the front stairs. She was now in the dining room at the French doors, trying to get out. I waited for her to stop again; getting up was harder than I thought. I felt as if I hadn't had any sleep. I was dragging.

When she didn't stop, and the clawing became more frantic, Cockapoo started wailing, and Foxy started barking again. It was then I realized Heidi was having a serious problem. I jumped off the couch and startled Cockapoo and Foxy. Foxy was standing on the side of the couch with Cockapoo next to her.

Still exhausted and half-asleep, I bolted to the closest door, which was the backdoor. I put my hand on the handle, jiggled it, and called for Heidi to come so I could let her out. The clawing sounds by the French doors suddenly stopped. I yelled again and waited. I was waiting for her to come running through the kitchen, but instead of Heidi coming, Rocky came running down the back staircase. He stopped behind the couch in the family room.

Evidently, it was Rocky I had heard earlier going up the back stairs. He stood in the family room with Foxy and Cockapoo, quietly listening and staring at me. I found it a little strange that Rocky didn't run to the door to go out since he always wanted to go outside and had to be the first dog out the door.

I yelled for Heidi again and jiggled the door handle, but still, nothing moved. There were no sounds of Heidi running across the tile floors. I waited a few more seconds, and when she still wouldn't come, I went to the dining room to look for her. When I reached the dining room, she wasn't there, standing by the French doors. I looked under the dining room table and at the top of the stairs. I also peeked into the office. I walked up the front staircase a few steps and called her again, but still, there were no sounds of Heidi or anything moving upstairs. *Where did she go?*

Back in the family room, I could hear the dogs barking and whimpering again. I figured that maybe Heidi had gone down the back staircase and was now in the family room with them. I walked back through the kitchen and into the family room, but still, Heidi wasn't there. *Where is Heidi? Why can't I find her? I thought.*

I called her again, and still nothing. I went back to the dining room, and now the other dogs followed. I looked at the French door curtains, and that's when it occurred to me that maybe Heidi was locked outside. Perhaps she was clawing at the doors, trying to get into the house. Somehow, she was left out when Dean and I went to sleep. *How could this have happened? Poor Heidi!*

I went to the French doors, pulled open the curtains, and looked out, but I didn't see her. I opened the door to call her, but the other dogs pushed me out of the way. They rushed out the door with their hackles raised aggressively, barking. They ran around the yard while I kept calling for Heidi. It was early afternoon, and the neighborhood was quiet except for them barking. *Where is Heidi?* I looked at the forest, and then a horrible thought crossed my mind; Heidi was frantically trying to get into the house, and now she was missing. It was time to wake up Dean. I quickly called the dogs back into the house, locked the door, and ran upstairs. Rocky went with me.

When I reached our bedroom door, it was locked. Sometimes Dean locked the door to keep the dogs out while he was sleeping. Rocky and Heidi can open the doors by pushing down the handles, and they would jump on him to wake him up. I frantically banged on the door and yelled, "Wake up, wake up, Heidi is missing! Something happened to Heidi!"

Dean quickly staggered to the door while still half-asleep. He opened the door and asked, "What about Heidi?"

Just past Dean, lying on the bed, Heidi was looking at me, shocked and emotionally upset. I looked at her and said, "Didn't you hear me calling you?! Why didn't you answer?"

She rolled over, wanting me to pet her belly, while Rocky ran under the bed. I asked Dean if he had opened the door to let her in the bedroom, but before he could answer, I stated, "She was just downstairs clawing at the doors. Her clawing woke us all up. I was panicking because I couldn't find her, and I thought she was missing."

He said, "No, I don't know what you're talking about. She's been sleeping quietly next to me all day. It wasn't her clawing."

I sat on the bed next to Heidi to calm down while my mind raced. Dean looked at me and asked if I was okay.

"No," I replied.

I was trying to figure out if it could have been a nightmare. *Was I hearing the clawing in my sleep?* No, it wasn't a nightmare. The dogs also responded to what they heard. They were trying to warn me; they knew all along it wasn't Heidi clawing.

5
Dark World

Dark moving images in forest

After the clawing incident, I informed everyone in the house not to assume it was the dogs clawing at the doors. I said, "Always check before you open the door to verify it's the dogs and not something else."

It was another warning added to the house. We had so many in our home that it was like living in a hostile third-world environment. I could hardly believe we were living this nightmare, and just when we thought it couldn't get any worse, it did.

~~~

On March 7, Adam was working late again. I was in the office with Dean when the phone rang. I answered, and he whispered, "I'm in the bathroom at my job, and there's noise on the other side of the wall. It sounds like someone is running up and down it. Whatever it is, it's in the storage room next door. The storage room door is also banging; it sounds like someone is opening and closing it. I can hear it just outside the bathroom. The scary part is. No one else is in the building. Stay on the phone with me. I'm going to try to get out of here, but I'm waiting for it to stop. Then I have to secure the building and get my stuff. Listen to this."

He held up his cell phone so that I could hear it. I was horrified. I whispered, "Are you sure no one else is in the building?"

He replied, "I'm positive. I've already checked the building twice. There was a lot of activity tonight. I just had to use the bathroom before I left. I went into the bathroom, and it started scratching the wall. I listened to it and thought maybe it was a rat, but then it started running up and down the wall and banging the door."

Frantic, I covered the phone and quickly told Dean what was happening. He picked up the extension phone. Dean let Adam know he was also on the call.

"Okay, hi, dad," Adam whispered.

Dean and I quietly stayed on the phone with Adam listening to the banging and his breathing. I frantically prayed for the activity to stop, and then it did.

After it stopped, Adam stayed in the bathroom for a few more minutes to make sure it was gone. He quickly repeated what happened to Dean and said, "I'll call you guys back. Wish me luck. I'm going to try to get out of the building." Then he ended the call.

Dean looked calm even though he wasn't, while I, of course,

began to panic. I asked Dean what time it was so I could estimate the wait. I figured it should take no more than five minutes for Adam to get to his truck and call us back. I started pacing and said, "We knew something like this was going to happen; why didn't he listen?!"

Dean and I had warned Adam about the ghost in his building from the very beginning.

~~~

In November, Adam started working for a new company as a software engineer. The first few weeks he started and worked late, he told us some disturbing things about his new work building.

Outside the building, a large section of forest lined the edges of the parking lot. The parking lot was 'L' shaped, wrapped around the building. Late at night, walking to his truck gave him a creepy feeling. Adam told us, "Some nights, I get the feeling something's watching me from the woods. It's the same feeling I have when I come home at night and the Bigfoot are around. The hair on my neck and arms stands up, and I can't wait to get into my truck and lock it."

Adam began parking closer to the building, next to the entrance. At that time, he was unaware of the paranormal activity inside the building. Evidently, at night the building was creepy inside and out.

After Adam and Amanda broke up in December, he began taking on extra work projects and staying late more often. It was then that he started to hear strange noises inside the building.

He said, "It sounded like someone running through the building wearing windbreaker pants."

He could hear the wind moving. Later, he often heard what sounded like someone working, typing, and touching things in two of the cubicles near him.

Adam worked in a large room divided by cubicles. The cubicles were six by six square with five-foot high walls. He also often heard noises in the back offices.

At first, Adam would leave his cubical and check to see if someone else was working in the building. He would head towards the sounds, but when he got there, the sounds would be behind him on the opposite side of the room. It happened a few times. When he tired of chasing the sounds, he decided to ignore them. He also avoided the back offices since they gave him the creeps. He figured he wasn't technically alone but told us, "Nothing could be worse than seeing a Bigfoot." Boy, was he wrong!

As the weeks passed, the sounds escalated, and so did the activity;

evidently, ignoring them only worsened things. When the subtle sounds no longer scared Adam, strange blurry moving images appeared behind him, reflecting on his computer monitor screens. Adam used several monitor screens to work. When this happened, he would leave immediately. It happened more than a few times.

One day Adam told one of his co-workers that the building was haunted, and with deadlines on projects looming, the co-worker had to work late. He worked a few nights alone in the building and told Adam he would never do it again. The building gave him the creeps, and he heard strange sounds all night around him. He would walk towards the sounds to investigate and then hear them behind him on the other side of the room. He also felt someone was watching him over his shoulder. Adam's co-worker warned him not to work late; we also warned him, and he did listen for a while. He told us he would leave when the cleaning crew left at 7:30 p.m.

One night before he left, Adam talked to the older woman in charge of the cleaning crew. He asked if she had noticed anything strange. She told him a strange car had parked in the parking lot a week before, evidently making her nervous. Adam explained he was referring to something else. When he mentioned the noises in the building, he said her eyes opened wide. She replied, "Yes. I don't tell anyone about it, but yes, there is something in the building. I can't keep good help; they all quit."

She reminded Adam of the young girl he had met who had worked with her the previous week. The young girl quit after an incident. The older woman told Adam what had happened. Evidently, they were done cleaning and about to leave the vacant building. They turned off all the lights, picked up their stuff, and walked a few feet towards the side door when all the lights suddenly went back on. It scared them since they were only a few feet away from the only light switches in the building. She told Adam, "I couldn't leave the building with the lights on, so I had to run back to the switches and turn them off again, then quickly get out of the building."

She mentioned why she didn't say anything to the client -- she needed the work. Adam told her he understood. Sometimes he too had to work late to meet his deadlines.

Her story fascinated me, and I told Adam I wondered how many cleaning people had to deal with this problem. After all, they clean vacant buildings that may be haunted at night, and if they say anything, they could lose their jobs. I felt sorry for her and worried about Adam. Adam told us not to worry; we had enough to worry about, but of course, we did.

~~~

Finally, the phone rang after what seemed like an eternity. Adam was safely in his truck on his way home. I talked to him for a few minutes; he was okay, so I handed the phone to Dean. I needed to calm down. Dean spoke to Adam until he pulled into the driveway.

After Adam came into the house, we talked again. He was unnerved but not enough to heed what we told him.

I said, "Whatever is in the building doesn't want you there after dark. It's getting angry, and you must forget about your deadlines or work from home."

Adam explained that he needed a more advanced computer to work from home. He was saving for it and would buy it soon. When I asked how much money he needed, I nearly choked and replied, "You are kidding me?!"

Dean and I both warned him that it was only a matter of time before something worse happened. Adam knew we were right, but argued and blamed his demanding deadlines. Even after suffering this horrible incident, he believed he could handle it. He said, "I've experienced a lot worse."

We shook our heads. Adam told us, "If I hear any noise, I'll just leave. It made noises all night, but I ignored it."

He accepted that the ghost in the building was angry, but he would try not to irritate it. He said, "I have a job to do regardless."

How could we argue with that? We sure knew what regardless meant. It meant that despite the horror and personal fear, you had to function normally, similar to the older woman who cleaned the building. You have to do what's expected, such as going to the store, working to pay your bills, running errands, and meeting your deadlines.

We were all living in two worlds. One world moved around us while the other scared us half to death.

6
The Phantom Act

Jack's old food dispenser

By the end of March, the forest appeared vacant during the day. I hadn't seen anything moving in it for weeks and wondered if the creatures had relocated. Unfortunately, the only way to know was to go into the woods and check. Going into the forest was always a risk, but worrying about Adam and the creatures at the same time was just too much stress. I needed some relief, and thought I would have one less thing to worry about if the creatures were gone.

~~~

On March 29, Dean and I crossed the street and entered the forest to the right of the pathway. I was a bit nervous, but I had watched the woods all morning, which appeared unoccupied. There were few trees, and most of them were bare. Once inside the forest, the fallen leaves made little sounds as we walked. The bright sun lit the forest bottom with nothing above or heads to obstruct it. There were a few twisted vines, broken limbs, and toppled trees.

Only one tree immediately stood out from the rest. The treetop was missing, and the bark was stripped. The tree had two dug-out holes on the side of it under where the top used to be, and in one of the holes, there was a spear-like stick protruding from it. I'm no expert in trees, but it looked like the sharp stick was placed there on purpose. The stripped sections of bark reminded me of the camouflage materials the creatures used to hide. *(Photo chapter 1)*

Further back in the forest, Dean saw Jack's old food dispenser. It was still hanging from the tree where Jack had abandoned it. I was amazed that it was still there after more than a year of extreme weather. I could hardly believe that the limb holding it was still attached, especially since most of the other large tree limbs around it were gone.

We walked a little further and took a few pictures. That's when I noticed something else I found strange. The mounds of dirt that looked like graves were missing. We couldn't find one anywhere. It was as if they never existed, and even the tree stumps that looked like grave markers were gone.

To me, the forest looked as if it had been wiped clean except for the strange-looking tree. Before we left the forest, Dean and I agreed that it appeared as if the creatures had relocated. He said, "Now the question is where did they go?"

"Anywhere but here if we're lucky," I happily replied.

Seeing inside the forest gave me some peace of mind.

~~~

With the forest quiet and vacant-looking, I wanted to stop recording audio every night and only record randomly. It was a good idea, especially after I saw how many recording devices we had, all the recorders looked the same, and I thought we only had a few. I didn't know that whenever I ran out of recording time on one device, Dean bought a new one. I counted as he pulled them out of the drawer. We had seven in the drawer and two by the monitor; each could record over forty hours; we had hundreds of hours of audio still to go through. It felt so overwhelming that I placed the devices back in the drawer and closed it. The last thing I wanted to do was document them.

In fact, I had no energy to do anything. I felt I was suffering from a new form of exhaustion, relief the creatures were gone, lack of sleep, and worrying about Adam. I could barely keep my eyes open. Dean was concerned and suggested I should try to get more sleep. He would stay up at night and watch the house in case something happened. I agreed, and it was a good idea in theory.

~~~

On April 4, I woke up, although, at the time, I didn't know what time it was; all I knew was that it was dark outside. I was disappointed when I found out it was 11 p.m., early evening, and not just before dawn. I had hoped to sleep all night instead of only a few hours.

Worried about Adam, I went downstairs into the office. Dean was sitting at his desk playing his game on the computer. I asked if Adam had made it home safely. He said yes. I sat at my computer for a few minutes, staring at the cameras. I was so exhausted that my perception seemed foggy, and I really needed to return to bed.

I couldn't hear any sounds coming from the monitor. I asked why it was so quiet. Dean said he turned off the audio due to the heavy static; listening to it was annoying him. I knew what he meant.

Some nights, the static sound was so loud that it wasn't worth listening to the microphone. Dean looked at me and said, "Go back to bed; you're exhausted."

I replied, "Easier said than done."

I was used to being up all night and couldn't go back to sleep. I told him I just needed a cup of coffee. I headed for the kitchen and then rummaged through the refrigerator to get something to eat. It would be a long night again, and I was dragging. I returned to the office and put on my headphones to listen to a previous recording. I also started working on the computer, doing some writing. Dean put his headphones on to listen to his game. I glanced at the cameras, and everything appeared to be fine. With the audio off, it was going to be a quiet night.

With all my attention focused on the computer and unaware of the time passing, I was interrupted when suddenly I heard the front door banging. It started banging back and forth. Obviously, someone wanted to get into the house but forgot to unlock the deadbolt. The front door handle was disengaged, but the engaged deadbolt was pounding against the doorjamb.

I looked at the camera screen and saw no one on the front porch, and unfortunately, due to the shape of the porch, the camera couldn't view directly in front of the door.

The door stopped banging for a few seconds and then started again. Since it was somewhat of a familiar sound but startling, I thought it was Adam returning home from work carrying something. Sometimes he forgets to call and doesn't always turn the key all the way, causing the deadbolt to catch. After it stopped again, I took off my headphones, looked at the door, and thought, what the hell is Adam doing banging the door like that? He's going to break it!

Dean stood up from the other side of the desk. I figured he was going to open the door for Adam, but when I looked at him, he appeared upset. Then I remembered what he had told me earlier. Baffled, I asked, "I thought you said Adam was home?"

I heard "Click-click" as he pulled the slide back on his pistol to chamber a round. He had his pistol in his hand. I didn't see it when he stood up; the computer monitor was in the way. He quickly came around the desk, leaned towards me, and whispered, "Adam is home. It's 3 o'clock in the morning."

My mind shrieked in horror the split second I realized that wasn't supposed to happen! I jumped away from the desk to the other side of the room. Within seconds, Dean stood a few feet from the front door with his pistol pointed at it. Now realizing we were in grave danger, I frantically yelled, "Wait! Don't open the door!"

I was in a complete state of fear and panic. I needed my gun on the bookshelf a few feet away. He waited a few seconds while I stepped forward, grabbed my gun from the bag, and held it with both hands to control my shaking. Now wide awake and alert, I kept my eyes on Dean the door and the cameras. I saw nothing walking across the porch, the front lawn, or the street. Dean glanced at me, and I shook my head no, indicating I saw nothing on the cameras.

Dean cautiously leaned into the door and peeked through the peephole. Within seconds, he backed away and shook his head, indicating he saw nothing. He pointed at the French doors and gestured with his finger that he would circle around to the side of the front door. He wanted to look through the fence.

I nodded okay. I knew that whatever was trying to get into the house needed to be stopped immediately!

He grabbed the flashlight on the table and headed toward the French doors. I watched the cameras, and still, nothing went by them. By the time Dean unlocked the French doors, Rocky and Heidi were standing next to him. They came tearing down the front staircase. He opened the French door, let the dogs out, and went outside behind them.

Terrified, I anticipated hearing frantic barking and gunshots. When I didn't, I thought something terrible had happened to Dean, Rocky, and Heidi, and maybe they needed me. The French door was slightly open, and the curtains covering them were moving. The silence was creepy, and the horrifying thought of a Bigfoot coming through the door hit me for a split second. I maneuvered closer to the doors to cover them with my pistol and listen for Dean. The silence seemed like an eternity, but it was probably only a few seconds.

Foxy and Cockapoo, who were still quiet in the office, suddenly rushed the French doors. They ran past me and headed outside. The second Foxy went out; she started barking a warning bark. Rocky then started barking, but his barking didn't sound urgent, and the other two dogs were quiet.

A few seconds later, I saw a light beam crossing the cameras. It was the light beam from Dean's flashlight shooting over the fence. He was okay! Relieved, I took a deep breath. Dean was shooting the flashlight in multiple directions, the front porch, up and down the street, and into the forest. When he finished, he returned through the French doors and said, "No one's at the door."

He quickly walked to the front door, opened it, and stepped outside. I locked the French doors and followed him but stood in the front doorway. I could hear the dogs on the other side of the fence peeking through the wood slats, nervously whimpering and barking. They appeared as moving shadows blocking the light between the slats.

The front porch motion sensor lights were bright. The bright lights filtered across the front lawn and the street, but it was dark and eerie, where the light ended at the forest edge.

Dean walked along the front porch toward the driveway. He again shot the flashlight at the forest, street, and dark areas next to the house, including the porch roof. I watched his back and waited. It was as if I had seen this horror movie before, Dean, outside in the middle of the night, armed and searching for creatures. Finally, he returned and said, "It's gone."

I stated, "How is that possible? It was just banging on the door, trying to get into the house, and it didn't cross the cameras! Where did it go?!"

"I know," he said.

He locked the front door and went to the French doors to call the dogs. They came in, and he locked the French doors too. He walked into the office, cleared his gun, and put it in front of him on my desk. He was standing at my desk, anxiously staring at the cameras. I carefully put my gun next to his and quietly sat on the couch beside Rocky. What the hell just happened? *I thought.*

The only thing we knew for sure was that it wasn't a person. Nobody could've moved that fast and known how to avoid the cameras. The amount of girth needed to bang the door back and forth so violently led us to believe it was one of the creatures. Also, pushing and holding down the door handle required fingers. It tried to get inside the house again, but the deadbolt stopped it.

Mr. Hill had warned us about this, and it was one of my worst nightmares. A Bigfoot at our front door, I couldn't believe it had just happened, and I wasn't even paying attention.

I told Dean, "I thought it was Adam coming home. I could have opened the door! Honey, thank God you were here," as I began to meltdown, "I didn't know what was happening. Why did it do that?"

Dean didn't respond as I began crying and shaking, then pathetically, I uttered, "I can't even imagine if the door had opened and a Bigfoot walked in, I would have died. Why did it shake the door? Why did it do that? What did it want?"

Dean walked over to the couch and gave me a hug. Rocky jumped on both of us, licking our faces. Rocky was just nervous. Dean went into the bathroom to get me some tissues. When he returned, he gave them to me, walked over to his desk, and sat down.

He looked at the cameras and said, "When I heard that door, I already knew Adam was home, and none of our neighbors would be shaking our door in the middle of the night. If that door had opened, I would have emptied a clip in whatever walked through it. I didn't know what was coming through the door, but it was about to meet its maker."

I sniffed my nose, wiped my eyes, and said, "We're lucky that when we replaced the front door, we reinforced the doorjamb. I can't believe it blatantly tried to open the door with us sitting right here! It knew we were here! They can hear us in the office."

I wiped my eyes and sniffed again, "That thing banged the door and left without us seeing it. How did it do it, how can we defend the house if we can't see them? How are they getting so close? How do they talk in the microphone, leave footprints by the pool, and get around the cameras without us seeing them? And where did it go?"

Dean shook his head and said, "Honey, I don't know where it went. There are so many dark places outside where it could hide. I wish it would show itself to me - just once."

"Not me! I wish they would hide, but I don't call that hiding!" I cried. "Those things think they live here; they think this is their house! What are we going to do? We can't sell the house with creatures banging on the doors and drinking from the pool. We're never going to get out of here, never!"

"I don't know what's happening or why," Dean stated, sounding frustrated.

I cried, "I wish these things never existed. They are monsters! Destroying people's lives, or worse, they are relentless beasts, and something is wrong with them. The way they move and hide, I can't even get a video because they look like blurred darkness moving. They are so creepy!"

I fell over on the couch with Rocky licking my face. Gasping for air, I muttered, "I wonder how many families are suffering. People are suffering, and those things are breeding, and there is no way to stop them. No one can stop what we're going through."

After my emotional meltdown, Dean comforted me as best he could. He, too, was upset. He covered me with a blanket and later sat beside me, stroking my head until I finally stopped crying and fell asleep. Needless to say, he stayed up all night watching the cameras with his gun in front of him.

7
The Creepy Crawler

Camera viewing the front door and handle with deadbolt

The next day, Dean took the camera off the fence and placed it in a planter box on the side of the front door. This way, we could view the door and the handle just like the French doors. I also asked him to place heavy furniture against the front and French doors at night. I wanted to barricade the doors to slow down any creatures attempting to breach them.

Dean and our sons moved the furniture every night for about two weeks before Jack brought it to my attention; it served no purpose other than to make me feel better. We had tile floors, and the furniture, when pushed, would slide across them. Of course, Jack demonstrated this by pushing the front door open with the furniture behind it.

The problem was that I felt defenseless against these beings and wanted to do more than just add another camera. Still, the camera seemed to work, just like the one covering the French doors. They stayed away from them. We ordered another night vision camera to shoot across the front porch to replace the one Dean moved, and we bought another twenty-inch television.

I was struggling to move past the door incident; there were so many questions. Such as the obvious one; why didn't it break the door down? Again, the creature tried to enter through the door, just like before, when it pushed down the French door handle. Doors and windows would not stop them.

For whatever reason, I felt they couldn't break through the doors or windows to enter the house. Maybe they feared leaving evidence behind of their existence. Or perhaps they also had rules to follow and couldn't break them, other than for revenge, such as us shooting one.

So why did it bang the door? It was so terrifying not knowing the reason. There had to be one, and then it dawned on me that we went into the forest the week before the incident. Retaliation was the only reason I could think of, considering the creature seemed angry but angry enough to risk a bullet. That part made no sense but it would explain why it left so quickly. I think it was the alpha male, and he just wanted to scare us. Maybe he knew the deadbolt was locked, or even more disturbing, he didn't.

Either way, I believe it was a warning to us, "We're still here, so stay out of our forest! We're watching you, and you're no threat!" If so, then the message was received loud and clear. We could only assume they were back despite the forest looking vacant.

However, it was just a theory that helped me to get past the incident. Although, after what the creature did, I thought about what happened to Jack a year ago. When after an incident, he insisted, someone opened the front door and then closed it. I recalled...

One day, Jack went into the forest to look around. It was sometime in the afternoon, and no one else was home at the time. He went through the front door but didn't lock the deadbolt because he didn't have his keys. Rocky and Heidi were standing by the door as he left. He made sure he closed the door and engaged the handle latch. He said, "I made sure it was closed."

He was in the forest for only a few minutes when Rocky came running down the path. He grabbed Rocky to drag him home while also calling for Heidi. He didn't know what happened but figured the door must have opened somehow. Heidi would have followed Rocky, but Cockapoo and Foxy would have stayed in the house. They were older and not prone to wandering (and couldn't get far if they tried). He was worried that he couldn't find Heidi but decided to get Rocky home first. He wanted to check the front door, ensure Foxy and Cockapoo were safely inside, and then look for Heidi.

When he saw the front door, he was bewildered because it looked closed. He pushed on the door, and it didn't open. He had to push down the handle's thumb press to open the door. He went into the house with Rocky. Foxy was lying in the office with Cockapoo under the desk. He called for Heidi and then quickly checked the other exterior doors in the house. They were all locked. He was about to go look for Heidi when suddenly, she came running down the stairs. She was in the house the whole time. To this day, Jack insists that "the door was closed." He said, "Someone or something opened the door, let Rocky out, and then closed the door behind him.

If a Bigfoot opened the door, it would explain what happened and how Rocky found Jack in the forest. Jack was right; he did secure the door, but the creatures didn't want him in the woods. That's probably the reason why they let Rocky out.

Over the years, I wonder how many times the creatures could have opened the front door. When we first moved in, the deadbolt wasn't always locked. I had to insist that Dean and our sons lock it every time they left, especially during the day. It required a key, and they felt it was unnecessary because our home was mostly isolated. Cars rarely passed, and the city was underdeveloped, but I felt otherwise. Now I'm glad I insisted, and we added the reinforced locks.

The more I thought about Bigfoot and door handles. The more I questioned other things they could have done, such as the year our vehicle batteries died repeatedly. Dean kept replacing them, but it didn't stop happening until he locked the doors. I figured someone was opening the doors at night, causing the batteries to drain. Could Bigfoot also operate vehicle door handles? If I asked Mr. Hill, he would probably say; what do you think? They have hands, don't they? And I would respond, yes, they do, and some beasts even have claws. It's weird how something so obvious can be overlooked.

In the meantime, the terror continued, but it was not what we expected.

~~~

It was just after dark, and I needed some papers from William's room. He had just come downstairs to get something to eat, so I went upstairs to get them. I quickly went up the back staircase and down the hallway. William's room was the last room at the end. I flung open his door, stepped inside his room, and then heard something. It stopped me cold, and I froze as his door slowly closed behind me.

I could see his entire room due to his ambient lighting. His laptop was sitting on his desk in front of his couch. He had papers scattered throughout his desk area, with his glasses, empty water bottles, and a coffee cup. It was apparent he had been working before he left the room.

Just outside the window across from his desk, I heard it moving. It abruptly moved the moment I opened the door. His blinds were pulled up, his drapes were tied back, and his window was cracked open a few inches. Startled by the sound, my eyes immediately focused on the window, but I couldn't see out of it. All I could see was my frozen reflection staring back.

In the darkness outside, it was moving along the outer siding. Clawing, grabbing, and bending it. It was traveling to the left of his window, towards the corner of the house. With each sound of movement, my eyes followed the walls to track it. It was trying to get away from the window.

I also wanted to get away, and when I could finally move. I forgot the papers, slowly backed out of his room, and ran downstairs. Frantic, I ran into the kitchen and told William, "They're watching you from your windows! You need to close them!"

William ran upstairs to close his windows as Dean asked what had happened. I began to tell Dean, and William quickly returned to listen. When I finished, Dean said, "Well, that would explain why the siding along the back of the house keeps falling down, no matter how many times a year we repair it."

Dean and William went outside to check the backyard with flashlights. They looked up at the exterior siding but saw nothing.

For the rest of the night, I had a sickening feeling knowing that a conscious being was outside Williams's window watching him. I would have never expected anything to be there. William's windows were along the backside of the house and sat over two stories high, with nothing below them but siding.

The scariest part of the incident, aside from it being there, was that I had the feeling that whatever it was, it never expected to see me open the door. I think it lost its grip, and that's why it moved. "It" was definitely expecting to see William again.

~~~

A few weeks later, Dean had a doctor's appointment. He always scheduled his appointments early to be the first patient of the day. He left at about 6:30 a.m., and afterward, I lay on the couch in the office watching the cameras until I fell asleep.

Around 9 a.m., I was awakened by a loud bang, and the wall behind the couch shook. Startled, I nearly fell off the couch, and my heart started racing. Immediately, I thought earthquake or sonic boom? I quickly looked around the room to see if anything else was moving, such as the light fixture attached to the ceiling, but it wasn't. Then I realized it couldn't have been a sonic boom. I wasn't in California or living on a military base anymore.

When I looked at the camera's monitor screen showing the outside, everything appeared fine. All seemed calm and quiet. I switched the monitor screen to view the driveway. I saw Adam's truck; he was still home asleep, and I assumed so were Jack and William since they had no plans that morning. Under the desk,

Cockapoo was awake watching me, and so was Foxy. She was lying on the floor next to the couch. Rocky and Heidi were nowhere in sight. I sat back on the couch to calm my heart and gather my thoughts.

I listened and looked at all the walls in the office, trying to figure out what had just happened. The only thing I could think of was that something big intentionally hit the wall behind the couch. It hit hard enough to wake me up, but how could that have happened?

The wall separated the inside of the house from the garage. It also extended ten feet outside along the front porch. It helped to form part of the front porch cove. However, based on the location of where the wall was hit, the front porch was unlikely.

Realizing the only plausible answer, I jumped off the couch and backed away from the wall. I took a second look at the camera screens. I saw no one outside in front of the house, but was the garage door open? I couldn't tell if the garage door was opened or closed. The camera showing the driveway was mounted over the top. It was possible that the garage door didn't close when Dean left, and a Bigfoot got inside and hit the wall.

Dean could have pressed the button for the door to close and witnessed it moving downward, so he left. However, the door will automatically reopen if something breaches the bottom sensor. It was a safety sensor to prevent the door from closing and injuring small children or pets. In the past, objects placed against the door have fallen in the way causing the garage door to reopen. Everyone in the house knew not to drive away until the garage door closed completely, but maybe Dean was in a hurry and didn't wait.

Regardless, I just needed to stay calm and check the garage. I grabbed the pistol and peeked around the corner into the hallway. The hallway door to the garage was closed. I quietly approached the door and placed my hand on the handle. Slightly pushing it down, the handle didn't move, and I could feel it was locked. I stood there, holding the handle, trying to decide what to do; I was too afraid to open the door to the garage.

I thought, nothing's outside, everything is fine, and the garage door is probably closed; just open the door and check, but I couldn't do it. Even though it would have only taken a second, I didn't want to open the door. I figured with my luck, Bigfoot would have been standing on the other side of it.

Quietly, I backed away from the door and snuck back into the office to put the gun down. It was time to wake up Adam, Jack, or William so they could check. I was about to leave the office and run upstairs when suddenly, I saw Dean pulling into the driveway on the camera. He had to pull the car into the garage, I thought. I went back into the hallway, waited a few seconds, unlocked the door, and opened it. The double-car garage door was already open.

I was relieved to see Dean pulling the car into the garage, and he was pleased to see me standing in the hall doorway. After he parked, he said, "Hi honey, I'm surprised to see you're still awake, and did you know the garage door was open?"

8
Adam's Hauntings

Illustration of Adam sitting at his computer

By June, there was no doubt that the creatures were in the forest again. The forest pathway was disappearing, and the thick, overgrown foliage provided cover for them. I could see movement behind the first set of trees on certain days. I tried to get a video of them, but every time I did, they shook the limbs of the trees and sometimes violently.

On June 20, at 1:10 a.m., Dean and I were in the office when we heard the familiar sound of a train whistle. The train tracks were about 1.5 miles away, and many trains traveled thru at night. It blew once, and then an eerie symphony of howls began as it blew again. The bizarre howling continued for a few seconds and then stopped.

I quickly jumped out of the chair and set a recording device by the monitor. Then grabbed Rocky; he woke, barked, and jumped off the couch. I held Rocky and pet his head to keep him quiet. Heidi also woke but ran out of the room, and our other two dogs just listened.

I wanted to record the howling to identify the animals and tell how far away they were and from which direction they were heading. Since many animals were involved. To our relief, they sounded miles away, and the pack didn't seem to be moving. Thank goodness, because the sound they produced had a chilling effect. In all the years of recording, we had never heard a sound like it before.

When I replayed the recording, I heard no sounds of Bigfoot in the pack, but maybe they were Dog-man? Although, Mr. Hill did tell us that Bigfoot likes to holler when the train's whistle blows. He said, "It helps to drown out their vocals." *(Screaming howls)*

Regardless of the animals' origins, it was a chilling reminder that nothing would change as long as we lived in this neighborhood. The beasts were always going to be lurking somewhere nearby. And unfortunately for us, they weren't the only beings lurking.

~~~

On July 11, the phone rang. It was Adam calling; he was driving home from work and sounded strange. He said, "Hi mom, I'm just calling to let you and dad know that I saw something tonight that really scared me. My hands are shaking and I can barely hold the steering wheel. I'm okay now, and I will tell you what happened when I get home. Can you put dad on the phone? I need him to talk to me while I drive."

I repeatedly asked, "What happened?"

He replied, "Right now, I can't talk about it. I need to focus on driving. Please put dad on the phone."

Upset, I handed the phone to Dean and started pacing. Dean spoke to Adam about insignificant things, and he calmed him as he drove. Thirty minutes later, Adam finally pulled into the driveway safely. Dean was outside waiting for him while I stayed in the office pacing.

As they crossed the front porch over the microphone, I heard Adam say to Dean, "You won't believe what happened."

I flung open the front door and said, "What happened? What did you see?"

Adam struggled to get past Rocky and Heidi; they were eager to greet him at the door. He hung his computer bag on the staircase banister and petted the dogs. He looked fatigued and stressed. Dean went into the kitchen to get him something to drink while Adam began to tell me what had happened.

He said, "I was sitting at my desk working and listening to my music on my headphones. I hadn't realized that it was getting late, and everyone had left for the day. I turned off my music and the building was quiet. I figured so long as there wasn't any activity, I should continue working. I have a huge deadline on a project due in a few days."

When Dean returned with his drink, we all moved into the office to talk. Rocky and Heidi had calmed down, but Foxy and Cockapoo were waiting for their pets. Adam petted them and then sat on the couch. He told us he worked a few more hours and then started to hear noises in the building. He said, "It sounded like wind blowing through the building; it was weird."

I shook my head and said, "You promised you would leave the minute you heard something."

"I know, I know," He replied.

He sighed and continued, "I looked around but didn't see anything. So I sat back down to continue working. But the sounds got louder and louder, except this time it sounded like someone running. The hair on the back of my neck stood up, and I knew it was time to call it quits and get out of the building."

He then quickly packed up his stuff and headed for the side door. He was about to shut off the lights and head out the door when he got a bad feeling. He said, "It felt like something was waiting outside the building by the door and it was worse than whatever was inside."

I asked, "You mean something from the forest?"

The parking lot at his job was surrounded by forest. Adam had mentioned before that the woods around the building at night gave him the creeps.

He replied, "I don't know but I felt trapped because I didn't want to walk outside the building to my truck."

His truck was parked near the front door on the other side of the building. He decided to turn around and walk back through the building.

He said, "I knew I was going to encounter something, no matter which way I went, but I figured if something was going to kill me. Then at least inside the building, they would find my body in the morning," he nervously laughed.

Dean and I both told him that we didn't find that funny. He said, "I know, but that's what I was thinking."

Dean and I shook our heads, and Adam continued. "I turned off the lights and started to walk back through the building towards the front door."

I said, "Wait! Why did you turn the lights off?"

"The light switch to the building is by the side door," Adam replied.

"What do you mean? There's no light switch by the front door?" I asked.

"No, but the building has all night lighting, or what you would call emergency lights, so you can still see," he replied.

I commented on how stupid it was to build a building with no light switch by the front door. I was distraught that Adam had to walk through a dimly lit building.

Dean agreed, and Adam continued, "So I turned off the lights and started walking through the building towards the front door. I turned the corner to walk down the hallway and saw a dark entity. It was standing in the middle of a T-intersection at the other end. I froze and stared at it. It looked like a silhouette of a young girl."

He then described that it was less than five feet tall with long hair and completely black. He couldn't see any facial features, no eyes, or anything. He got the feeling it was a girl.

He said, "It reminded me of an image I had seen in a movie

where a girl comes out of a well. I can't think of the name of the movie."

I said, "I know what movie you're talking about, I can't think of the name either, but I can picture it. It must've been terrifying."

"Well, that's what she reminded me of," Adam said as he took a deep breath and continued, "I watched her and she just stood there facing me. I kept looking for her eyes, but she didn't have any. She was blocking my way to the exit. Although I didn't get a bad feeling from her, which I thought was strange."

For some reason, he wasn't that afraid.

He said, "She finally turned to her left and went down another hallway that leads toward the back of the building. After she left, a cold chill went down my back, and I sensed something else was in the building coming from behind me. I needed to hurry down the hallway and get out of the building. I took out my knife and started to walk down the hall towards the exit. I didn't know what else was in the building, but I figured if it was physical, then I wasn't going down without a fight. Really, I didn't know what was going to happen but I felt better carrying my knife in my hand."

Dean asked, "Where was your gun?"

"It was locked in the truck; we can't take guns in the building," Adam replied.

Frustrated and upset, I asked, "What good is a gun or knife against a ghostly entity? And those dark ones are really bad according to some television shows. They can appear as anything. It chose to look like a young girl for a reason, but that's probably not what it was. They are dangerous, and now that you've seen it, it's only going to get worse! It's just like all the other creepy things in this neighborhood. They choose to show themselves. It was only a matter of time before you saw something in that building. That building is scary."

"Yea, it is," Adam stated, "but I haven't even told you the scariest part yet."

I said, "What, you mean it gets worse than that?!"

"Yes!" He leaned back on the couch, rubbed his face, leaned forward again, and said, "Yes, it gets worse than that."

Adam and I both took a deep breath, and he continued, "So, I started walking down the hallway toward the T-intersection, hugging the wall along the left side. When I got to the intersection where she went, I looked down the hallway. I couldn't see a thing.

It was pitch-black. It was as if someone had cast a dark curtain over the hallway entrance and I couldn't see behind it."

Adam explained what the area should typically look like at night. The positions of the emergency lighting, exit signs, and ambient lights glowing from the kitchen vending machines at the other end of the hallway. Evidently, it was all gone, even the wall formed by the office cubicles along the right side of the hall. From what he told us, it seemed as if half the building had gone missing. He stated, "I know what the building should look like at night."

After he looked down the intersecting pitch-black hallway, he felt pressure as if something was trying to pull him back to the hallway from which he came. He quickly went down the opposite hallway and headed towards the front doors. He could see the double-glass doors of the building and his truck parked outside them.

He left the building so fast that he didn't even remember, pulling out his keys and unlocking his truck. He said, "I jumped in the truck, locked the doors and sat there a few seconds to calm down. I was just about to call you and leave when it dawned on me; I didn't check the double doors to make sure they were locked. Sometimes the doors don't close all the way and you have to pull them together. I couldn't leave the building without checking the doors."

Adam paused, took a drink of his tea, and said, "Now, this is the part that really scared me."

He took a deep breath, "So I got out of the truck with my gun to check the doors. I pulled the doors together to lock them, when all of a sudden I noticed something moving above me. It was against the glass door inside the building. I looked up and saw a distorted face pressed sideways up against the top of the door. It's hands were up against the glass as if it was trying to push the door open and get out of the building, but instead it pushed itself backwards and vanished. I wouldn't have even noticed it with all the reflection from the outdoor lights, but it moved and caught my eye. I was terrified. Its face looked distorted and evil. I think he was the one I sensed behind me in the building. The girl, like I said, wasn't that scary, but that second one...that second one... scared me half to death. That's another face I don't ever want to see again."

Audio Book 3 Chapter 8

9
The Hunting Club

Deer along easement

Adam stayed home a few days before returning to work after the incident. He also purchased a new computer that was less expensive to work more from home. He tried very hard not to work late from the office, but eventually, weeks later, he did.

Adam explained it had to do with the computer servers and the program upload speed. He also needed access to specific programs he could only use at work. I was upset with him and the company. I believed Adam had an impossible workload, and the company was taking advantage. I didn't fully understand the problem, so all I did was worry.

Dean and I constantly called Adam every time he stayed late, but so far, all the activity at his job had stopped. He kept reassuring us the building was quiet, so we need not worry. I told him, "That's what also bothers me. Why the sudden change?"

Things did seem to be changing, just like the seasons. We were experiencing times of calmness, followed by horrifying incidents perpetrated by dreadful things. It was like hitting a lottery of horror; we were just trying to survive.

I spent my days watching the creatures hiding in the forest, rearranging it, and camouflaging, using the thickness of the foliage to their advantage. They were changing the forest drastically from one day to the next. It was like watching an army preparing to attack, but they didn't. All they did was sway the trees, shake the branches, and watch people driving by or jogging past our house.

~~~

One morning, I decided to peek out the window; it was a spur-of-the-moment decision. Two young women were jogging past our house just before sunrise. They were new joggers to the neighborhood, but I had seen them before, and they usually turned around at the corner. I was curious to know if the creatures were watching them.

After they passed, I went to the window in the family room, cracked the curtains, peeked at the forest, and waited. When the women returned and jogged past again, two reflecting eyes inside the forest were following them.

I couldn't see the creature inside the forest, only its eyes, as it swiftly traveled over forty feet. The eyes of the beast began at the forest pathway and disappeared at the end of the forest by Steve and Becky's house. Since I only saw the eyes reflecting about four times between the trees as it vertically crossed, I figured it had to be big. I also thought it was traveling on all fours since it wasn't very tall. The eyes were moving about four feet above the ground. The entire incident only lasted a few seconds, and it was chilling. The creature moved swiftly without shifting any branches on the trees.

It was also shocking. The women had no clue a creature was in the woods stalking them. I was amazed that they never even glanced at the woods or our house as they ran past.

After they left, I realized that most people were unaware of monsters lurking in the woods, especially in a housing area. People see houses in a neighborhood and think it is safe, but it's not. Trees and bushes provide the best means for anything to hide during the day and especially at night. If the women knew they were being followed, they would never jog past a forest again. I guess no one ever told them that predators hunt and hide where you least expect, and they do so in silence.

~~~

On August 7, at 1:46 a.m., a family of deer appeared on the camera. They were walking on the easement outside of the forest. We had seen this family of deer before, and I always videoed them. I would set my handheld camera on the desk tripod and hit the record button.

I usually videoed all the animals we saw at night in the neighborhood, including other deer, a family of raccoons, two little foxes, and all the cats.

Whenever I saw the deer grazing along the easement, it gave me a feeling of joy and relief. I figured if the deer were there, the Bigfoot wasn't. The deer, I thought, would have detected them by eyesight, smell, or sound.

This family of deer consisted of three doe and one fawn. They always arrived from the direction of Mr. Drake's house. Therefore, I assumed they were coming from the park across the street from him. They traveled slowly, grazing and romping, heading towards the forest pathway's direction. They were precious and healthy looking, especially the little fawn. I watched them for a while and then returned to working on the computer.

Assuming no Bigfoot were around, I set an audio device early in the morning before going to bed. Later, when I listened to the audio, the only thing that was recorded at 5:37 a.m. was a weird *birdcall*.

~~~

A few days later, I told William about the deer. He had also seen this family of deer before on the camera and liked watching them. I downloaded the video, and we watched it on my computer together. The video footage was twenty minutes long, but the deer only appeared on it for the first several minutes. We watched them until they went off-camera. They were a pleasure to watch, and we enjoyed seeing them together.

After the deer left the camera view, William left the office, but I continued watching the video. William was in the kitchen when I yelled, "Come back. There's something else on the video!"

He returned to the office, and I backed up the video to watch it again. Exactly ninety seconds after the deer left the camera view, a large shadow of a figure walked from the direction of the forest to the street. It stopped in the middle of the street, just off-camera to the left. As if it knew how to avoid the camera.

We couldn't see what cast the shadow, but it was walking upright in the shape of a broad person. After it stopped seconds later, a smaller, more agile-looking shadow approached it. The smaller shadow came from the same direction but appeared contorted due to how it awkwardly moved. It disappeared into the shadow of the larger one, reappeared, and went back toward the direction from which it came.

The larger shadow was carrying something, maybe a stick or a club. It raised it above its head, placed it back down, turned, and walked back toward the forest. It was a shocking and disturbing end to an otherwise joyful video.

After watching it, we were somber and upset. We knew it wasn't a person walking out of the forest at 1:53 a.m. with a creepy-looking child carrying a primitive weapon. *(Bigfoot Hunting)*

I told William, "They were hunting the deer. I thought the deer would sense them. But they had no clue they were around. I hope some of them got away."

William said, "I really hate that forest," as he left the room and walked back into the kitchen.

Audio Book 3 Chapter 9
Video Bigfoot Hunting

10
Final Warning

Foxy with Cockapoo after a swim

For the past few months, Foxy's health had deteriorated due to old age. We kept her happy and healthy as long as we could, but now she was having a hard time. She was struggling to get up and down. She wasn't in pain, but her quality of life was slipping away.

She quietly slept next to me in the office most days and nights. Sometimes during the night, she would frantically raise her head to listen. When she heard the sounds of the Bigfoot, she would try to stand and make it to the door to go outside and bark at them. She hated hearing the creatures and wanted to keep them away.

Sitting on the floor beside her, I tried calming her down. I pet her head and give her lots of kisses. I tell her she's a good girl. She taught Rocky and Heidi about the creatures and other important things they needed to know. She did her best with them, and we were forever grateful.

I thanked her for all the love she gave and all the nights she protected us, especially when we had no clue the creatures were around. I told her she was courageous and the most incredible Bigfoot warning dog ever, but I understood she was tired. She looks at me with her big, brown eyes as if to say, "I don't want to leave you because I'm worried. Who will protect you when I'm not around?"

I tell her she's going to a better place where she need not worry anymore. We love her with all our hearts and don't want her to worry. Dean and the boys lay beside her, petting her head and rubbing her back. The vet said it was only a matter of days before we would have to put her to sleep. Her body was wearing out, and we didn't want her to suffer.

A few days later, she could barely raise her head, and it was time to say goodbye. All our hearts were broken. We had the pleasure of loving her for over thirteen years. Dean and Jack placed her in the car while William, Adam, and I stayed home. Rocky, Heidi, and Cockapoo were quiet and sad. I think they understood what was happening. They could tell by the tears in our eyes as we waved goodbye.

Dean and Jack took Foxy to the park before taking her to the vet. Dean drove slowly through the park while Jack sat in the backseat with her and opened the car door. He said, "She really enjoyed seeing the park one last time."

The house felt empty when they returned home without her, and our hearts were broken. Part of our family was missing, and it would never be the same again. I cried and thought about the day we met her...

We were living on the Air Force base and saw an ad in the paper that listed, rescue dog needs loving home, approximately four years old and housebroken. We had just lost one of our dogs to cancer, and our other dog was all alone. Dean phoned the ad, and we arranged to meet her.

The day we met Foxy, she was fragile and could barely raise her head. We were told that she was found starving in the forest. She looked as if she had lost her will to live. Dean sat on the floor and called her in a loving tone. She approached him and mustered up the energy to lift her head and wag her tail. We could tell she had been through a lot and needed a loving home. The rescue organization had already taken her to the vet. She had all her shots and was healthy but forty pounds underweight. A glimmer of hope with big brown eyes was all she had.

We fell in love and took her home. We knew she was exceptional. Within a month of hugs, kisses, and loving pets, she had gained fifteen pounds, and three months later, she was the picture of health. One hundred and ten pounds with the most beautiful auburn coat.

...Foxy was happy, loving, and caring. We loved her very much, and so did Cockapoo. Foxy was the only reason we had Cockapoo in the first place. She wanted Cockapoo as her baby, and Cockapoo wanted her as well.

It was all quite amazing; we adopted Foxy, and a year later, she adopted Cockapoo. I remember it well, and I can still picture them playing in the yard together when they were younger.

Cockapoo, at the time, was about six months old and had lived a few blocks away; she belonged to friends of ours who also lived on the base. They were going on vacation for two weeks and asked Adam if he would take care of her. After school, when Adam arrived at their house, he found Cockapoo in a cage behind their couch.

He took her out of the cage, played with her, and brought her home. He couldn't bear to put her back in the cage and leave her alone, especially for two weeks. When Adam walked through the door carrying Cockapoo, Foxy was interested. Her motherly instincts took over as she licked and sniffed Cockapoo from head to toe. Cockapoo was excited to see Foxy as well.

Adam could hardly hold Cockapoo as she wiggled to get down, licking Foxy back. It was obvious they fell in love the second they met. But for us putting them together was a little unnerving. Foxy was giant, and Cockapoo was a tiny, five-pound ball of fur with eyes. We were afraid Foxy would hurt her accidentally, but she didn't. Foxy was a gentle giant when it came to Cockapoo.

Foxy took good care of her for two blissful weeks, and they played all day. Foxy would lie down so Cockapoo could climb on her to wrestle. Cockapoo would nip at her face and chew on her tail. Foxy would place half of Cockapoo in her mouth, and seconds later, she would immerge unscathed, a little wet but extremely happy. All they wanted to do was play and be together.

When the two weeks were over, Cockapoo had to go back home. Foxy was sad as she waited by the front door. The next day, I heard scratching and faint tapping along the door's metal screen bottom.

I opened the door to see what was tapping the screen and was shocked to see it was Cockapoo, covered in dirt from head to toe. I didn't know she knew the way to our house. She had to have traveled two blocks and crossed two streets by herself, and she was tiny. I would call the family and give Cockapoo a bath. While Foxy watched and waited for me to finish so they could play outside.

Over the next few weeks, Cockapoo would arrive at our house whenever the family put her in their yard. She would dig out no matter how long it took and appear covered in dirt. Somehow, Foxy always knew she was coming and would be waiting for her by the front door.

Again, I would call the family and bathe Cockapoo while Foxy would sit by the sink and wait. She reminded me of a worried mother making sure her baby was safe as Cockapoo wiggled in the sink, trying to escape. After the bath, the two would play all day until the family could come to get Cockapoo, usually after the workday ended.

Eventually, the family gave up trying to keep Cockapoo in the yard and asked if we would keep her. We loved Cockapoo and said yes.

After all, there was no way of keeping Foxy and Cockapoo apart. They were meant to be together until the end. We were all meant to be together as a family.

As I sit here with my shattered heart, I can still picture them playing in the yard. They were so happy. In the end, all we had left were our memories and pain. Foxy was a gentle, loyal, loving soul with a kind, strong heart. Losing Foxy was the worst feeling in the world, but I couldn't have imagined a life without her.

Sleep tight, my little girl, until we all meet again.

11
Out of Town Visitor

Location of where the ghostly image appeared

One of Dean's best friends, Jim, an old Army buddy from Texas, was planning to visit. He and Dean had known each other for years and frequently talked by phone after they retired. They mostly talked about military stuff and current news events. He was going to stay with us for a week and didn't know anything about our Bigfoot situation. Dean asked, "Should we tell him before he arrives?"

I said, "No, it would be too difficult to explain by phone. Not to mention, he might not visit if he knew."

We hadn't had any visitors in almost two years. December 2012 was the last time my family visited for William's graduation. Before discovering the creatures, my mother would visit at least three times a year and stay a month at a time. We all enjoyed her visits and missed having company. I particularly missed spending quality time with her, shopping, eating, and watching our favorite movies. But now, due to the Bigfoot, she refuses to come until we move. Most of my family refuses, and I don't blame them. Even I didn't want to stay in this neighborhood. Although our situation had improved considerably from the beginning, it was still unpredictable.

We also had no social life either; staying up all night and sleeping during the day left no room for friends. Jim was the only one and was more than welcome to visit.

Soon Jim arrived, and we were happy to see him, especially Rocky and Heidi. They loved meeting him since he gave them lots of attention. We sat in the kitchen for hours talking before Dean showed Jim the house. When they entered the office, Jim noticed the cameras and the television screens. He asked about them, and Dean began to explain. He told Jim about the clan of Bigfoot across the street and the other beasts. Jim was stunned and kept repeatedly asking the same questions.

Jim said he hadn't thought much about Bigfoot and was surprised the creature existed. We showed him pictures and videos we had captured of the creatures and listened to some audio recordings. I gave him copies of my books while Dean told him the story of how it all began. Jim was a little upset with Dean for not telling him sooner, but at least it gave them a new topic of conversation. Dean told him in detail about some of our more terrifying incidents. We stayed up all night, talking and watching the cameras.

Over the next few days, Jim recovered from his initial shock and was somewhat jazzed to be up all night watching out for the creatures. However, for us, it was becoming challenging. Jim kept saying, "I want to see a Bigfoot," and he wanted to explore the forest.

Dean and I tried to explain why going into the forest wasn't a good idea. I feared the creatures' retaliation. The Bigfoot hadn't bothered us in months, and I didn't want to risk upsetting the beast. We stayed inside at night and out of the forest during the day. The strange arrangement seemed to work for us, but unfortunately, Jim refused to heed our warnings despite my reservations.

One afternoon I took a nap and woke up to find Dean and Jim missing and the truck parked in the driveway. They had to be around somewhere since they were walking. I suspected they were in the forest, so I called them. Dean explained that after they returned from the store, Jim got out of the truck and walked into the woods. Dean followed him with his gun, concerned about his safety. They were in the woods and would return in a few minutes.

I understood why Jim, who didn't live across the street from the creatures, would find them entertaining. He was going home in a few days, but we were staying. For us, the danger was real; but for him, it was just an adventure. What happened with Jim was a perfect example of why we didn't tell people. If we did, we would have a forest full of people provoking the Bigfoot and then going home, leaving us to deal with the creature's retaliation. I hoped for the best but expected the worst. I was more disappointed than angry when they returned, and I was worried.

On the other hand, Dean was somewhat glad they went into the woods to look around. He found quite a few drastic changes in the forest that were interesting. He explained that it looked like a typical forest on the right side of the path with no broken branches or fallen trees. It was thick, but they could easily walk through it.

However, it was impassable on the left side behind Steve and Becky's house. Dean said, "We couldn't go two feet."

He described a massive thicket of broken branches, sticks, and weeds, with twisted vines and toppled trees. The thicket was approximately fifty feet long, piled against the tall trees, bridging the vacant spaces between them. It was a barricade, wide, tall, and thick. He said traveling behind our neighbors' houses on the forest side was impossible. The only obvious way to get behind them was to walk down the middle of the creek, and they decided not to do it.

I said, "Well at least we know what side of the forest has Bigfoot in it. Let's just hope they stay on their side."

It seemed ironic. The Bigfoot built a barricade to keep people out, and I wanted it to keep them in the forest. I guess we both agreed; Bigfoot and people don't mix, just like bringing to life prehistoric beasts in modern times. There were movies about that, and the people were eaten.

Jim was thrilled to have gone into the forest, but constantly warning him about the beast was turning out to be a daunting task. Some nights he wanted to sit outside on the front porch and yell at the creatures, hoping to irritate them. Dean had to talk to him a few times. He was turning out to be quite a handful.

Until one night, Jim finally saw something that blew his mind. It was something he never expected to see, and it appeared on the camera pointed at the forest. We both saw it. I had seen them before, but it was a life-changing experience for him. He was so stunned that he couldn't stop talking about it to this day. It happened on the night of September 28 around 2:48 p.m.

Dean and Jim were talking in the kitchen while I was in the office writing. William came into the office to give Cockapoo a treat. She was lying under the desk. When William glanced at the camera screens, he noticed what appeared to be an apparition. He watched it for a few seconds and asked, "Does Bigfoot cloak?"

I stopped what I was doing to answer him, "I don't know, why do you ask?"

William said, "Because there's a strange outline of a ghostly image walking back and forth across the street, right now on the camera."

He pointed at the area on the television screen that displayed the night vision camera viewing the forest. I looked at the screen, and William was right; something transparent was walking. I caught a glimpse of it before it disappeared. I grabbed the handheld camera to record the screen. While William went to get Jim in the kitchen so he could see it. Jim ran into the office and started asking questions. I tried to answer him while setting up the camera to record, but his questions were distracting. I said, "Just watch the camera screen!" as I pointed to the area on the screen.

At that moment, the ghostly apparition appeared again. Except this time, it was more apparent. It looked like a man walking, wearing khaki pants and a plaid shirt. It appeared on the easement, took four steps toward the forest, and vanished before reaching it. It happened so fast, within seconds, and the handheld camera was still warming up. Jim immediately asked, "Did you capture it on video?"

I said, "No, the camera started to record after it disappeared."

Jim was upset that I didn't capture any video but was shocked that he saw a ghost. He said, "You saw what I saw, right? It took four steps and then disappeared before reaching the forest. It looked like a man walking. It was a ghost. I never expected to see a ghost. It was the ghost of a man."

I reassured Jim that I saw it too and it was a ghost. I said, "The camera is now set up to record the screen just in case it shows up again."

He took a deep breath, stared at the screen, and said, "If you had recorded it, it would have been the best ghost footage ever recorded. It was so clear."

Jim repeatedly expressed his disappointment that we didn't capture any video of the ghost. I explained how difficult it was to capture anything strange on video. Especially ghosts, since they often appeared and disappeared within seconds. I said, "Most of the time, I set up the handheld camera to record the monitor after we see something. Capturing anything on video was all by chance, even if the cameras recorded 24 hours a day, who would look at the footage?"

I pointed out that I am only one person. We didn't have the resources to view nightly video recordings. I told him, "We probably miss things all the time on the camera since we only glance at them during the night or when we hear something. Logically there could be Bigfoot, ghosts, and dark moving shadows constantly going across the cameras but if we don't see them. How would we know?"

He understood, especially after he saw the ghost, and realized how quickly it appeared and disappeared.

I said, "I have spent many nights questioning what just passed through the cameras. After all, this entire neighborhood is full of scary things, but as long as they stay outside, I try not to worry about them. I only worry about the ones that can kill us."

After I finished explaining, Jim left the room to tell Dean what we saw; Dean was busy cooking something for them to eat in the kitchen.

~~~

Later and for the rest of his visit, Jim repeatedly told Dean, William, Adam, and Jack about the ghost, even though William had seen it too. Jim was so thrilled to have seen one he told anyone that would listen everywhere he and Dean went. He called his wife and told her as well.

In the end, I was happy for Jim. He had seen something most would never see in a lifetime, but sadly, for me, it was just another night in the office.

12
The Faceless Beast

View of neighbor's carport from bathroom window

Dean and I remained optimistic about selling the house and moving away. The house needed repairs, and we had a to-do list, such as fixing the unsightly cracks in the driveway. We decided it was time to work on them. We placed concrete patches and glue in the gaps and then painted the slab. It was a long process, and everyone in the house had to park in the street for about two weeks.

~~~

On the night of October 24, I was alone in the office, typing on the computer. Dean wasn't feeling well, so he went to bed early. Rocky and Heidi went with him, but Cockapoo stayed with me. She was asleep under the desk in her little bed.

William and Jack were also home but upstairs. They knew their dad had gone to bed, leaving me alone on the bottom floor of the house. They also knew that if something strange happened. They wouldn't hear me yell from the office, so they took turns coming downstairs to check on me. I wasn't too afraid of being alone, it had been quiet lately, and I had the cameras and microphone. Also, I was waiting for Adam. He was at the cinema with friends, and I expected him home a little after 11:00 p.m.

At 11:10 p.m., Adam arrived home and parked in front of the house to the right of our mailbox. His truck was the furthest parked away from the house. I watched on the camera as he exited his truck, crossed the front yard, and cut around the flower bed to get to the front door.

After greeting Adam at the door, we went into the office to talk. I turned off the front porch microphone to listen. He wanted to tell me about the movie. We talked for a few minutes before he said goodnight and went upstairs to bed.

After he left, I decided to straighten up the office and file some papers. I circled around the desk towards Dean's side to open the file drawer. I was standing with my back to the cameras, reading the files, and placing the papers when I had a strange feeling that I needed to stop and look at the cameras.

I quickly turned, looked at the camera, and saw a huge face staring at it. It was black, light, blurry, and moving. My instinct was to scream and run, but instead I froze. I couldn't believe what I was watching and thought, Lion!

The lion stood in front of the camera, mounted on the fence with its head tilted upward, looking directly at the camera and sniffing it. It turned, walked toward the front door, and sniffed at the bottom. It stood about four feet tall on all fours. It was huge! It had a dark face, a light-colored, slick-looking body, and long black hair around its neck. It was some type of lion at our front door. I thought *no one would believe this; what should I do?* I could run, video it, or watch it. I decided - video!

I quickly turned, reached across the desk, grabbed the handheld camera, turned it on, and hit the record button. I pointed the camera at the screen, but the beast was gone. *I thought; it has to cross another camera since it was just in front of the house.* I continued to record every camera screen, waiting for it to reappear. And seconds later, it did.

I captured the back end of the lion as it walked along the edge of our driveway towards the street. When it reached the street, it turned left and strolled down the middle towards our neighbor's houses. After the animal left the screen, I recorded a few more seconds and then panicked. I put the camera down and ran as fast as I could upstairs.

~~~

Frantic, I banged on Adam's door. He was still awake; I told him what had happened and then ran to tell Jack and William. When I told William, he said, "That's probably the large cat I saw earlier from the window. I was watering the plant in the family room window when I saw a large animal running down the middle of the street. I immediately thought 'lion' due to its size and the way it moved. I didn't have my glasses on and the thought of a lion running down the middle of the street?"

He made a face, raised his shoulders, and said, "I just thought it was the biggest cat I had ever seen. I was going to ask you if there were any large cats in the neighborhood."

"No-o-o, there aren't any cats that big in the neighborhood. Come look at the video!" I said.

~~~

They all followed me downstairs to the office to watch the video. Adam slowed down the footage and tried to enhance it so that we could positively identify the animal. It was difficult to see its head and face on the video, but they all thought it was a mountain lion. I disagreed and kept telling them it had a mane. I thought it was an African or Asian lion. Unsure of the kind of lion on the video, they wanted me to send the footage to someone who could analyze it. Even though we all agreed it was a lion.

I said to Adam, "Do you want to know what's really scary? That lion was tracking you. It traveled along the same path you did when you came home. It sniffed the air by the fence and the front door. It was definitely following your scent, and only fifteen minutes behind you."

Adam wears cologne, so he has a distinct smell, and I thought that's what attracted the animal. Adam said, "That's why I carry a gun, a knife, and a Taser. I'm prepared for anything. I would have killed that lion."

He and his brothers laughed. Of course, I didn't find it funny. They made other joking remarks as well. It went on for quite a few minutes, but when they imagined the lion fighting Adam, I couldn't help but laugh. I had to admit that it was a little funny. Joking was a way of dealing with strange situations in this house, which helped.

When they finished joking, the seriousness of the situation finally sunk in, leaving Jack and William worried. They told Adam and me that from now on, if Dean was asleep when Adam came home, we were to notify them the minute he arrived. So they could make sure he got into the house safely. Adam said it wasn't necessary; he would be fine. But they insisted, and I agreed.

We watched the footage together a few more times, and I told them, "Now we have a lion in our neighborhood. What is wrong with this place?! Why do these things keep showing up on our front porch? That beast scared the heck out of me. When I saw that huge head moving, I couldn't believe it! I thought it's the middle of the night, I'm alone in the office, and there's a lion at the front door. Only this could happen to me; it's the story of my life. I see the strangest things. I really need to start going to bed at night."

My sons smiled and said they were proud of me for being brave enough to get the footage. They all tried to make me feel better.

After Adam and William left, Jack stayed up with me in the office. He repeatedly watched the footage and compared it to YouTube videos of mountain lions. He said, "A mountain lion is what it looks like, we need to tell the neighbors."

I said, "Tomorrow we can notify the neighbors, but to me a 'lion' is no more dangerous than the Dog-man beast or Bigfoot. I think the animal was just passing through. Believe me; the other creatures are not going to tolerate a lion being in the neighborhood. Especially with their young one's around; the creatures will hunt that lion down and kill it, so I'm not overly worried. Although it is, disturbing and I do feel sorry for all the little dogs and cats left outside tonight. Even though, I worry about them every night."

So many things to worry about in this neighborhood; I'm amazed I sleep at all, even during the day.

~~~

Months later, a video expert looked at the footage and said it was a mountain lion. I respected his opinion because he had analyzed hundreds of videos over the years. However, I am positive the beast had a mane around its head. I saw the long dark hair when it was moving its head back and forth on the camera. I don't know how to explain it, but that's what I saw. The body, I agree, looked like a mountain lion, but even on the video, you can't make out its head. *(The faceless beast)*

(To date, I only saw the lion that one night and haven't seen it since. Over the years, I've been surprised by a lot of things. However, not seeing it again in this neighborhood full of creatures didn't surprise me at all.)

~~~

A few weeks later, it was Williams's birthday, and everyone wanted to go out to dinner as a family. We hadn't been to a restaurant as a family in over a year. We tried very hard not to leave the dogs home alone unless absolutely necessary. Especially after what happened to Foxy the last time we left. We usually took turns going out to eat. One or more of our sons would stay home with the dogs, and we would just order them a meal to go.

Dean kept reassuring me that having an early dinner would be fine. We hadn't had any problems with the Bigfoot in months. He figured that it would be okay if we were home before nightfall. We planned to eat at our favorite pizza restaurant, less than fifteen minutes away.

Before we left, I placed an audio recording device by the monitor and turned it on. If anything happened, we would record it, I thought.

I was very nervous as we backed out of the driveway and drove to the restaurant. But once we arrived, I saw families having a good time and wanted to be just like them. I wanted a glimpse of everyday life again. It wasn't so bad. I just needed to relax and stop worrying.

Eating out as a family was wonderful; it seemed as if no time had passed. We laughed, talked, and enjoyed a variety of pizzas we ordered. William ordered a pizza with anchovies and sat beside me, knowing it would make me cringe. I ordered a pizza with extra onions, knowing he would also cringe at the sight and smell. William and I had a fun time eating our favorite pizzas. However, I ended up with the short end of the stick. Dean sat on the other side of me and filled his plate with slices of each pizza, so I had anchovies on both sides. Adam and Jack also ordered their favorite pizzas.

After the pizzas, they all had desserts with a cup of coffee. The time passed very quickly, and soon it was getting dark. I looked out the restaurant window and announced it was time to leave. We settled the bill while everyone filled to-go boxes. Within minutes, we were on our way home.

~~~

I felt anxious as we drove home after the sunset, but I tried not to worry. We were only a few minutes late. Dean noticed I was quietly staring out the truck window and said, "I'm sure the dogs are fine," as he drove over the speed limit.

I thought about how anxious I felt whenever we came home, no matter what time or where we went. Turning the final corner and seeing the forest was such a dreadful feeling. It was a constant reminder of the "elephant in the room." No matter how hard I tried to forget.

Soon we were pulling into the driveway, and the house appeared okay. It was still in one piece, and the neighborhood was quiet. Dean opened the garage door, and we went inside.

~~~

To our relief, Rocky and Heidi greeted us at the door. While Cockapoo whimpered from under the office desk. She was waiting for her pets. Rocky and Heidi were overly excited, and Cockapoo didn't want to be trampled by them. We gave them all loving pets and leftover treats. We were delighted to see them as well.

After loving the dogs, I went to the office and turned off the recorder. I sat at my desk and listened to it while working on the computer. The recording was two and a half hours long. Dean later came into the office to play his computer video game. Inside the house, it was quiet, and outside seemed calm.

After two hours of listening to static, plus a few cars that drove by, I was getting sleepy. Dinner was relaxing, and I overate. I kept yawing, fighting to keep my eyes open. Dean told me to go to bed; he was wide awake and would stay up. I said I would, but I just needed to finish the recording. I only had twenty minutes left to go. He asked if I had heard anything. I said, "No, it's been quiet so far."

I yawed a few more times, and then five minutes later, on the recording, I heard Rocky bark. He barked and growled, and then strange mumbled voices and weird clapping sounds followed. Startled, I backed up the recording to listen to it again.

The second time I listened, I heard scratching before Rocky started barking. Something scratched to get his attention, and the mumbled voices sounded like chanting. I also heard sounds of something pushing against the window or French doors.

I continued listening past the chanting, and a few minutes later, I heard our vehicle pulling into the driveway. We were arriving home. *(Home alone)*

Now wide awake, I downloaded the recording to the computer and amplified it. I immediately recognized the creepy chanting sound. They were Bigfoot noises we had recorded before some of their vocals. They scratched the house and then pushed against it to threaten the dogs. I told Dean, "I found something on the recording, and it's bad. The creatures were here threatening the dogs."

Dean came around the desk and put on my headphones to listen. As he listened to the audio, he shook his head. When he finished listening, he handed me back the headset and sat down on his side of the desk, clinching his mouth closed. He was upset. I put my elbows on my desk, held my head, and closed my eyes.

I had an overwhelming feeling of guilt and sadness. I felt guilty about leaving the dogs and sad about our situation. There was no way we could ever leave the dogs alone again. The Bigfoot approached the house the minute the sunset. They knew no one was home to keep them out, and they took advantage of it.

Rocky was lying on the couch next to my chair. I turned around and gave him pets and kisses. I told him he was very brave and we were sorry for leaving them. He must have been terrified defending the house, Cockapoo, and Heidi, against the beasts. He rolled over, and I rubbed his belly and said, "You made Foxy proud today."

When Dean finally calmed down, we discussed what had happened. He felt the same as I did about not leaving the dogs again. We also thought it was strange that the creatures left only minutes before we returned. It was the second time that had happened. How did they know we were only blocks away from returning? It was perplexing.

When we finished talking, Dean gave the dogs praise and pets. He then went back to playing his game on the computer while I sat on the couch next to Rocky, watching the cameras.

I was quietly reflecting on all the strange things that had happened. Most I wished I could forget. When a car with bright headlights suddenly drove past the house, the bright lights flickered on the camera, reminding me of something else that had happened. I remembered...

It happened one night in December 2012; I had gone upstairs with the night vision scope to look for the creatures. I quietly entered our bedroom, not turning on any lights. I didn't want to wake Dean, and I feared that, somehow, the creatures would see the lights. I snuck into the bathroom. I tried to look at the yards behind our house through the window. A few nights before, I had seen dark shadowy figures in our neighbor's backyard and was looking for them again. It was slightly after 2 a.m.

The master bathroom window sat above our Jacuzzi bathtub. It was a small window 24 inches wide by 36 inches high, covered by a dark curtain. I had to stand in the tub to look out the window. It was challenging. The tub's sides were two feet high, and the oval tub on the inside was slanted. I had to be very careful getting into the tub in the dark while carrying the scope. It definitely wasn't one of my favorite viewing positions.

I was standing in the tub, repeatedly looking through the scope a few minutes at a time for several minutes. I looked at our backyard and neighbor's, the adjoining fence line, and the corner tree. It all appeared calm, and I didn't see anything unusual. The neighbor's house behind us was completely dark, and they were obviously sound asleep. I put down the scope and took another break for a few minutes. I remember thinking; I wished all nights could be this calm, quiet, and peaceful looking.

I picked up the scope to look out the window again when all of a sudden, the headlights of our neighbor's vehicle turned on. The car was parked in their carport on the side of their house, facing the back of our house. The bright lights immediately blinded me, and I quickly ducked out the window. It was shocking! A few seconds later, the lights went off. I waited a few more seconds before I slipped the scope back into the window and focused on the carport.

I saw dark, blurry figures moving outside the vehicle on the driver's side. I couldn't make out a definite shape or size. Maybe the car window was down, or the door was open, but I couldn't see it, and I saw no lit dome light inside the vehicle. I was watching the movement when the headlights turned on again. I ducked and waited until they turned off. It happened several times, and I kept ducking out of the window. The bright headlights from the vehicle were blinding me as I looked through the scope.

Finally, I put the scope down and opened the curtain slightly on the side to watch the lights and the neighbor's house with my naked eyes. Their vehicle lights kept going on and off; sometimes, they just flashed, and other times they stayed on for a few minutes. They were flashing in no distinct pattern that would indicate mechanical operation. No other lights in or near the house were turned on; the neighbors were still sleeping. It lasted for about fifteen minutes and then stopped. I climbed out of the tub and quietly went downstairs to the office.

...Thinking about that night, aside from the blurry figures, what still bothers me is the unusual pattern of the car's headlights. I kept reasoning that the dark figures had to be operating them.

Assuming they were Bigfoot and the car windows were down would explain what happened. After dealing with these creatures for years, I learned to never disregard anything, no matter how farfetched.

I now believe the creatures intentionally flashed the lights that night. Either they knew I was watching them and did it to stop me, or they were signaling to others nearby. Signaling to other Bigfoot was the most likely. Because I also wondered, after listening to countless hours of their banging and tapping sounds, if they used a form of "Morse code" to communicate.

Audio Book 3 Chapter 12
Video Faceless Beast

13
Primal Real Estate

Peeled tree along the front

On November 21, 2014, I realized that two years had passed since I first saw Bigfoot. It was the night our neighbors, Mike, Carla, and their daughter, Sara, ran towards the forest after Sara heard a raccoon scream. When they reached the forest pathway, two Bigfoot jumped from a tree. When they heard the beasts hit the ground, it scared them. Evidently, the magnitude of the sound was stunning.

Dean, Jack, Mike, and Mr. Hill searched the forest in pursuit of the creatures, but the Bigfoot had retreated and hid. When they finished searching, everyone went home for the night.

Later that evening, I was listening to the microphone in the office when suddenly I heard the creatures return. Determined to see them, I went upstairs with the night vision scope to peek out the window. It was horrifying seeing the creatures for the first time.

When I close my eyes, I can still see their beastly faces and bodies as if it happened yesterday. I can still picture the little beast sitting in the tree that appeared to be yelling from the treetop. There were so many Bigfoot in the forest I was terrified. I really wanted to see the creatures then, but now I regret it. I will regret it for the rest of my life. I wished someone had warned me that I didn't need to see what I wanted. I wasn't prepared to live with the consequences of my curiosity, and since I have felt damaged beyond belief.

So much has happened since the beginning, and it has been a never-ending nightmare. Like being on a rollercoaster ride that never stops, we were hanging on through every horrifying twist and turn. Not knowing what to expect after the sunset, we spent years waiting. We were waiting for something good to happen. It would have been nice for a change.

~~~

A week later, I was sitting in the office finishing some paperwork before bed. It was early morning, and Dean had already gone upstairs to sleep. Adam was awake, getting ready for work. He was about to shower, but before he did, he came downstairs and asked for medicine and a bandage. I asked why he needed them, and he replied that they were for some scratches. I inquired if Rocky or Heidi had scratched him. He said, "No, I've been waking up with them."

Stunned, I said, "What are you talking about? What scratches? Show them to me."

He put his right leg on the office chair and lifted his pajama pants. He twisted his leg to show me his calf. Across the calf of his leg, he had three and a half long, deep scratches. The scratches appeared strange because of the angle. You'd have to be double-jointed and definitely awake to replicate them.

He said, "I'm really getting tired of waking up with them. I also have some scratches on my back, but I only notice them when I take a shower, because they sting. Otherwise they don't really hurt me."

I asked if anything else strange was happening to him. He replied, "Yes, I've been having horrible nightmares and something keeps waking me up at 3:00 a.m. I wake up and look at the clock; it's the same time every night."

I shook my head and said, "We may have another problem. You shouldn't be waking up with those scratches."

I went to the bathroom to get the medicine and a bandage while he waited for me in the office. When I returned, Adam asked, "What other problem?"

I didn't mean to tell him, but Adam knew I was holding something back. I handed him the supplies and said, "Well, it's been brought to my attention that on one of the audio recordings I posted online, if played backwards, says something really bad. I don't know what to think of it."

He asked, "What does it say?"

I reluctantly replied, "It says 'I shall hurt them,' in a disturbing tone and then it laughs." *(I shall hurt them)*

"What!" he said. Let me hear it."

I went to the computer and played the audio. Adam listened to it a few times and said, "Yea, that's what it says, why didn't you tell anyone?"

I replied, "I just found out and I told your dad, but we thought it could just be a coincidence. It might not mean anything. Besides, we recorded that audio over a year ago. I just thought of it when you mentioned the scratches because it was on my mind."

Adam took a deep breath and said, "So you think it might be something else?"

I said, "I don't know but let me put a cross in your room over your bed, just in case. Do you wear your cross around your neck when you go to bed at night?"

He said, "No, I take it off because the chain tangles and it chokes me."

I stated, "Okay, I'll just put a cross on the wall over your bed. I'm not sure what's happening, so I'm not going to panic. Let's just put it on the wall and see what happens."

"Okay," he said as he suspiciously watched my demeanor and left the room to get ready for work.

I nervously smiled, but inside I was horrified. Adam knew I was panicking and didn't want to show it. I had no clue what was happening, but I knew nightmares, and waking up at the same time every night with scratches, probably wasn't a good sign.

I held it together until Adam left for work, and then I panicked and started pacing from room to room. I had given up on sleeping since that wasn't going to happen. I was waiting for Dean to wake up and come downstairs so I could tell him. I waited as long as possible before deciding it was time to wake Dean.

I told Dean what was happening to Adam, and he went downstairs and called him on the phone. Adam answered and said, "I knew mom was going to panic. Did she wake you up?"

Dean said, "Yes, she did, but it's okay."

They talked for a while, and Dean said, "We're going to put a cross over your bed and see if it stops. If not, we'll reevaluate the situation and go from there, but I'm sure everything will be fine."

After Dean hung up the phone, we agreed not to jump to conclusions, but the scratches were weird and really bothered me. Dean and I nailed a cross over Adam's bed. We figured, why take any chances? The cross could only help.

Later that evening, when Adam returned home, something weird happened in his room. He told us when he sat at his desk; a bulb from the recessed lighting above him fell. It hit him on the head and shattered. The bulb, he stated, didn't really hurt him, but he was covered in glass. He brushed himself off and cleaned up the glass. He said the incident was unnerving because it happened at the precise moment he sat at his desk.

What a strange coincidence I thought, that the day we placed the cross in his room the bulb fell. Maybe the bulb was loose? But hitting him directly on the top of his head seemed a bit intentional to me. I considered a more sinister answer; maybe it was a sign that something didn't want the cross in his room. Either way, the freak accident made me uncomfortable, but as the weeks passed, everything seemed to be okay.

~~~

Finally, in December, something amazing happened. I received a request to appear on a radio broadcast. They wanted to talk to me about the books I had written, documenting the creatures. It was a popular Bigfoot station, and the thought of doing the broadcast gave me tremendous hope; that someone listening could buy our house. Finding a buyer that knew about our situation would be the best possible outcome. So I agreed to do it. It just seemed logical.

On the day of the live radio broadcast, I was nauseous and nervous. I had never done anything like it before, and many thoughts ran through my mind. Most of all, I wanted to sound intelligent. I had been a homemaker most of my life and hadn't talked to anyone about our horrifying experiences.

Later that evening, as I waited anxiously, I checked the phone repeatedly to ensure it was working. When the call finally came, I did my best to explain our situation and answer questions. I found the host to be very nice, inquisitive, and knowledgeable. Talking with him gave me a sense of relief. Finally, I could articulate some of our experiences and warn people about these creatures. Doing the broadcast was a positive experience, even though it didn't change our situation as I had hoped.

~~~

In the meantime, we upgraded our cameras for Christmas. We purchased two more night vision cameras, a large flat-screen TV, a digital video recorder, and a new microphone. The new system could record the cameras 24 hours a day. Dean installed the cameras as the equipment arrived, and Adam put it all together.

As Adam set up the system, I was amazed that we would only need two televisions in the office. The digital recorder plugged into the large TV and divided the screen into nine channels. We could view and record up to nine cameras at the same time. The recorder also had other features, such as zoom; I could enlarge a specific area or watch just one camera on the large screen. We could also view the recorded footage for up to thirty days.

Since the digital recorder didn't have audio capability, the new microphone required a dedicated television. The microphone was attached to the camera near the front door. It was the only camera with audio that wasn't recording.

While Adam and I talked in the office, I asked if he had any new scratches. He told me no, and pointed out that I asked every day. He said the cross over his bed was working and he would let me know if anything changed. I said, "Okay, so I'll only ask you once a week just in case you forget to tell me."

We smiled while he focused on the wiring, although it was good news. When Adam finished setting up the system, he said we could add additional cameras later. I had six cameras on the digital system. He also added a wiring harness to keep the wires to a minimum, to help to make the sum of cameras less conspicuous.

Our realtor told us that prospective buyers would ask about the cameras when she showed the house. The buyers questioned if the neighborhood was safe. To explain the cameras, I told the realtor that there were animals in the forest and that we would watch them. Thank goodness she never asked what kind of animals.

~~~

When Adam turned on the additional cameras Dean placed around the pool area. It was obvious. The creatures were about to lose their pool privileges.

We always left the pool open and uncovered, even during the wintertime. The pool was too deep to drain and too large to cover for fear the dogs would run across it and disappear in the plastic. Also, a plastic cover wouldn't have lasted long anyway due to the harsh weather, snow, and rain.

At first, adding the additional cameras made me nervous. I wondered how the creatures would react, but as time passed, we didn't seem to have any problems. After all, it was wintertime, so the creek was probably full of fresh water for them to drink. I guess it was the best time to do it, before summer.

~~~

Soon I was scheduled to do another radio show. Of course, I was nervous and nauseous again, but little did I know I was about to learn an important lesson. Doing a live radio broadcast was similar to dealing with the beasts - always expect the unexpected.

On January 23, I did the next live radio broadcast. It was with the same host as the first one, although now he was hosting on a different radio station. It was a lot rougher than the first broadcast I did. I was surprised by some people "that supposedly called in to the broadcast" to ask questions. They didn't seem to want to learn anything; they only wanted to attack and use offensive language.

Initially, I was angry after the broadcast, but as I reflected, I became sad. I thought about all the other families in our situation that had no one to talk to and suffered in silence. The people who attacked me discouraged them from coming forward and telling their stories. Why would people do that? They seemed to only want to add to our misery without knowing any facts, although it wasn't all bad.

Some of the listeners that called were very encouraging. They were encouraging people just like me to come forward. I was delighted to hear from them, and in the end, they were the ones that really mattered.

The show host also surprised me. He offered to come to our house and bring a team of Bigfoot investigators. He mentioned they would arrive when the weather improved, maybe during the spring or summer. He also wanted to sit in the forest. Although I worried for his safety, I figured he would survive as long as he brought the investigators. I told Dean, "We must hold off on selling the house until after they arrive."

I assumed thousands; maybe millions of people listening to the broadcast that night would want to know that I wasn't lying. They were his fans, so I figured he would not disappoint them. I said, "They will come and help us, so we should wait."

(Unfortunately, we are still waiting and disappointed that we never heard from them again after the broadcast. Life was full of disappointments.)

~~~

Meanwhile, the new cameras provided some comfort because the creatures stayed away from them. Adam wasn't waking up with scratches anymore, and we were in contact with good people that listened to the broadcast. They were e-mailing me and offering advice, which I found very helpful and informative. Things were certainly looking up, and we had hope again.

~~~

By the end of February, I did another radio broadcast, which went much better than the last one. The radio hosts were nice and informative. We discussed many things, but I felt foolish when we talked about the damage inside the house when we first bought it.

The interviewers found the damage very interesting, just as Mr. Hill did when I mentioned it to him. I tried not to think about it, but deep inside, I knew we were all thinking the same thing. The creatures were probably in the house sometime before we bought it. Evidently, we missed all the warning signs that something was terribly wrong from the very beginning...

It was October of 2005 when Dean woke up one morning and saw the listing for the house. It stated it had six bedrooms, four bathrooms, and other rooms. We quickly dressed and drove to the city to look at the house's location and neighborhood. It was right in our price range and below market value at the time. The city was developing, and housing surveys called it the best community for family living. Jack was in high school while Adam and William were in college. We had just retired, so it made no difference where we lived.

We only intended to drive by when we arrived at the house, but a man was standing on the front porch. He went back inside, so Dean knocked on the door. The man answered, and Dean asked if we could look inside. He said they were about to leave but decided it would be okay, so he invited us in. He was a heavyset man and very polite. Within minutes, his wife was standing next to him. She introduced herself as they both began to explain away the condition of the house.

They told us about their seven foster children and some with special needs. I got the impression that some of the children were very sick and they were overwhelmed. The man explained that he hadn't done anything to the house in several years and let the children do whatever they wanted. He made it clear that the children ran the house. His wife just smiled and said, "So please excuse the mess."

Dean went one way and I the other as we tried navigating the mess. During my walk, two little girls that looked unkempt with very sad eyes followed me. I had the impression they wanted to tell me something, but they never said a word.

The clutter in the house was overwhelming, and it was hard to see all the damage. However, some of the extensive damage was hard to miss, such as the missing ceilings in the laundry room and sections in the garage. The man explained to Dean that the missing ceilings were due to water damage, and he assured Dean that the leaky pipes were fixed. There were also holes in some of the interior walls that were questionable.

Outside, the yard was atrocious, the swimming pool was black, and the white picket fence around it was in pieces. In addition, the entire yard was overgrown, covered in trees, dead leaves, weeds, and other debris. We were in a hurry when we looked at the house and knew that buying it in such poor condition would be an undertaking. Still, the location was excellent, the neighborhood looked great, and the price was right. I remember thinking; it just needed a lot of work and a good cleaning. Boy, was I wrong!

A month later, we were homeowners, and it took us another month just to clean the house enough to move in, and that's when the mystery began. At the time, no alarm bells went off. You would think we had never seen a horror movie before. It sounds cliché. I already wrote about the roof damage, but there was a lot more…

Aside from everything having to be replaced, such as the dishwasher, microwave, cabinets, toilets, and sinks, we found coals in the oven, which made no sense. The coals were piled at the bottom and burnt to a crisp. The inside of the oven was also black with soot that just the thought of cleaning it frightened me. I remember Dean saying, "There is no way," as he threw the stove out the front door. I commented, "Didn't they know how to turn the oven on?"

At the time, it all seemed overwhelming and very sad, and I couldn't help but question the foster care program in our state. Didn't they conduct home inspections? I could not believe foster children were being placed in this house. It's so ironic because that's what I found horrifying then. I guess I should have thought more about the other things we saw.

In the garage, where the ceiling sections were missing, we found no water pipes that could have caused it. In addition, there were strange holes in the drywall along the sides. The holes looked like someone had purposely punched through the walls. They varied in size and covered over fifty feet. Some holes were above the eight-foot level, and we couldn't figure out how or why someone would do that. We had to stand on a ladder and move it around the garage to repair them.

The double-car garage door was also damaged. Two glass panels along the top were broken, and the door was severely beaten and bowed. Reflecting back, I am so grateful and relieved by Dean's decision to replace the garage door with a solid, insulated one. I spent countless nights alone in the garage, painting trim boards, measuring things, and assembling items for the house. The creatures would have been watching me if Dean had picked another garage door with windows.

What a horrifying thought to know that after years of renovating the house, we were being watched. We often painted during the night with the windows wide open, especially during the summer months. Although we would close the windows on the bottom floor after painting for security reasons, the top floor windows would remain open. Somehow, the fumes needed to be vented. The constant construction smells like glues, stains, tile masking, laminates, and paints. I can't even recall all the strong odors.

We worked around the clock for years. I remember one year when Adam left for the summer. His room was under construction, with the windows wide open many nights. It makes me sick to think about it since his room sits directly across from the forest on the second floor.

I also recall all the exterior doorjambs and doors that were clawed with deep scratches and broken inside the house. As if turning a doorknob inside to open the door was a mystery. We replaced most of the doorjambs, doors inside the house, all the entrance doors, and doorknobs. How could a family have lived in this house?

It all seemed extreme, with broken appliances, toilets, cabinets, dings and holes in the walls, and dirt-stained carpets that couldn't be cleaned. Every light fixture and ceiling fan appeared petrified, including the curtains and rods held together by dust so thick that they still held their shape when we threw them out. Of course, everything had to be replaced.

We should have paid more attention to the damage or, at the very least, done a final walk-through before we bought it. Although none of it seemed to matter then, we had already decided to completely gut and remodel the house. The only problem was the kitchen and all the bathrooms had to be done quickly since we couldn't salvage a thing.

We also should have questioned why they had an alarm system on the house and each exterior door. The small magnetic door alarms above the doors beeped an annoying beep every time someone went in and out of the house. We removed them and disconnected the house alarm since we never had the code. When living in a large city, we knew that a few alarm systems could be expected, but not here in the South. Most leave their doors unlocked. We assumed the door alarms were used to track the children going in and out, but they could have been installed for another reason. Maybe the creatures were breaking into the house and opening the doors?

If this house could tell a story, what a horror story it would be; something terrible happened in this house to the family. Was it a slow and subtle deterioration or a chain of horrible events? Events that were so horrifying no one would have believed.

~~~

Instead of questioning the house's condition, we believed the previous owners when they implied their children were the cause.

I now believe, after reflecting, that they knew about Bigfoot and didn't want to tell us. Why would they? I kept thinking about what Mr. Hill said when I told him about the damage and some of the questions he asked. He asked if the garage was full of debris, similar to nesting materials. I told him, yes, it was full of something waist deep. It was so bad that Adam had to shovel it out. He filled up fifty-six heaping wheelbarrows full. Adam was so amazed that he counted them.

It was hard to answer when Mr. Hill asked if the neighbors had noticed anything strange. The neighbors thought the condition of the house was horrific and that everything about the family was strange. I told him of the twenty-two trees we removed that hid the property. The backyard alone was cloaked in darkness 24 hours a day. Dead leaves and debris knee-deep also covered the ground. Adam also had to shovel it out, one wheelbarrow at a time.

Later, when Dean reminded me, I recalled the neighbors did complain about the family to the city. I looked at Dean and shook my head. We both knew it was pivotal to our situation.

According to the neighbors, the family apparently dumped their trash in the water drainage ditch near the street. The neighbors complained to them when their trash backed up the water drainage. After that, the family dumped their waste in the forest. For years, the forest was their trashcan until, finally, the neighbors complained to the city about the smell. The city quickly responded and put a stop to it.

At this point, I could only imagine what might have happened after they stopped placing their trash in the forest. I don't think they knew what they were feeding until they couldn't feed them anymore.

You can't just stop feeding Bigfoot without repercussions. Mr. Hill once told us a story about people who fed them. He had investigated several cases over the years. He said, "It's all fine and dandy until something happens, and for whatever reason, they can't feed them anymore. People get sick, go into the hospital, grow old, or worse, die. It's the family who inherits the property or the person taking care of it that pays the price. The Bigfoot will run them out and destroy the property if they're angry enough."

Maybe that's what happened to the family who used to live in our house and us – the creatures became angry. The same terrifying cycle was repeating.

Jack and William placed food in the forest for years. I've been told it wasn't enough to feed a Bigfoot, but it was enough to feed the other animals, the smaller ones, the Bigfoot would eat. Jack also purposely fed Bigfoot the night he ran into the forest after Adam stood eye-to-eye with the beast. I guess the lesson of this story would be to never place food in a forest, especially in our neighborhood.

Audio Book 3 Chapter 13

14
Crypto Surveillance

Adam's bedroom windows and front porch roof

By the middle of March, I had done several radio broadcasts. Although exciting and informative, none helped to find a buyer for our house. I was grateful for the opportunity to reach people interested in Bigfoot. However, I was disappointed that our situation remained unchanged. Telling our horrifying story on the radio was therapeutic initially, but after a few times, it became emotionally draining, and I started having nightmares again. So I decided not to do radio for a while.

With all our terrifying experiences fresh in my mind, I began questioning whether we should sell the house to unsuspecting buyers. Even though we hadn't had any Bigfoot problems in months, selling the house without telling them about the creatures just didn't seem right.

Even though I believed the creatures tormented us for specific reasons, I couldn't be sure. Maybe it was only a matter of time before they threatened whoever lived in this dwelling. I told Dean that I would feel better if we told potential buyers.

He replied, "If we do that, we would never sell the house."

He pointed out that many families lived in the neighborhood and that new housing developments were being built next to the park. More families would be moving into the area, and we weren't responsible for them.

Logically, I knew Dean was right, but my conscience struggled; it was a battle within. It felt like I was being torn apart inside. One part of me wanted to run away screaming and get out by any means, but the other part was worried sick about the next family. I recalled old television shows I used to watch about haunted houses. They depicted true stories about families and their horrifying events. At the end of the program, it would sometimes state, "The family sold the house and moved away."

I guess it was supposed to make me feel better that the family got away, but it didn't. I always thought about the family that purchased the property and wondered if the ghost attacked them too. Maybe someone should do a television show about that.

Legally, I knew we were not required to disclose anything about the creatures, but morally it would be wrong. Dean said, "Is it wrong for us to want our lives back again?"

No, it wasn't wrong. I considered that even if we walked away from our home, the bank would sell it to another family. Either way, someone would live in the house, regardless of my tormented conscience. It was indeed a conflict.

I reasoned that at least the creatures were staying away from the house – and maybe, that was the best we could do for the next family. We could end the cycle of threats by resetting the creatures' boundaries. We had already done many things to discourage them, and it seemed to work, at least from our perspective.

~~~

On Sunday, March 29, Dean and I planned to go to lunch and then stop at the grocery store to pick up something for dinner. We took our morning naps and left that afternoon. All our sons were home, but we only told Adam we were leaving. His bedroom was just down the hall from the master bedroom. We wanted him to listen for the dogs in case they needed to go out. I knocked on his door, and he slightly opened it. He was awake and told us to have a good time and not to worry. He would keep an eye on the dogs and the house. We left and returned a few hours later.

When we returned, Adam was waiting for us. He said, "You won't believe what happened after you left."

I asked if everyone was okay. He said, "Yes."

Then he quickly helped Dean unload the vehicle, and we began putting the groceries away. Rocky was jumping around the kitchen, looking for treats. I petted Rocky and asked Adam if Rocky ate something he wasn't supposed to. Rocky eats anything he finds, especially if it's expensive and doesn't belong to him. I figured Rocky ate something of Adam's since he appeared upset.

Adam said, "No, it's worse than that."

He looked solemn. Then I noticed the gun on the kitchen island next to the stove. I asked why the gun was on the counter. Adam said he needed to explain. We all stopped what we were doing and sat at the kitchen island to talk.

Adam explained, "I was lying on my bed resting when you knocked on the door and told me you were leaving. I talked to you at the door and then went back to lie down again. I was thinking about going downstairs to get something to eat, but I wasn't ready to get up. I heard you leave out the front door and I heard dad start the truck and then you guys drove away."

He took a breath and continued. "The second the truck pulled out of the driveway, I heard footsteps walking across the front porch roof outside my windows. The footsteps were pounding –

boom, boom, boom, similar to when a person walks on the roof, but a lot heavier. It came from the garage, crossed the front porch roof, and then it went up to the next roof level above your bedroom. I was lying in the bed and I could hear it on the other side of the wall where the two rooflines meet. It scratched against the siding as it went up."

"Did you look out the window?" I asked.

"No," he said, "I heard it but I didn't want to see it. There was no way I was going to look out the window. I already knew what it was and I didn't want to see it. I just came downstairs, checked the doors to make sure they were locked, pulled out the gun, and sat with the dogs. I also checked on William and Jack and told them what happened. They came downstairs and sat with the dogs and me. They just went back upstairs when you came home."

Dean and I were speechless, but I understood why Adam didn't want to look out the window and see Bigfoot. Just the thought of it peeking back gave me the chills. Adam was right not to confront it. We suspected they were getting on the roof, but every time we searched the front porch roof with flashlights, we couldn't see them. Now we knew why - they were going up to a higher level. That would explain how they got close to the microphone without being seen. It would also explain where the creature went after it banged the front door. Adam explained a few more times what happened before he got up, handed Dean the gun, and said, "I'm going back to my room."

Dean and I thanked Adam for taking care of the house and the dogs. After Adam left, I told Dean, "It was on the roof in broad daylight. How did it do that without someone seeing it? People driving by could have seen it. It must have been lying down on top of the garage and figured we would see it, as we pulled out of the driveway."

Dean said, "It couldn't get down on the side of the garage without us seeing it. So it had to go up."

I stated, "You do realize it could still be up there. We can't see the top of the roof above our bedroom; its three stories high."

"I know," he said, "I think it's time to purchase more cameras and set up a wider perimeter."

I thought about the roof and said, "Do you remember the roofers we called to give us estimates on replacing the roof?"

"Yes," he replied.

I recalled, "The one roofer said that the roof above our bedroom was weird. It was worn in a way, he could not explain. Remember, he was trying to figure out why it looked so different, compared to the rest of the roof. That's what he was talking about – they're sitting on the roof above our bedroom. Oh my God! That would also explain all the weird sounds I heard in the walls."

Over the years, I often heard scratching sounds along the walls outside our bedroom. The sounds would move along the backside of the house, next to the chimney. It sounded like animals scratching and moving inside the walls or against the siding. I knew the chimney was behind the one wall, but something was moving around it.

I couldn't figure out where the sounds were coming from. I remember lying in bed during the night, listening to them while Dean was sleeping. I figured it was some kind of animal but hadn't thought much about it over the years. I guess it was something else I should have recognized as strange when we first bought the house. Back when I heard the sounds more often.

I asked Dean, "Do you think they're listening or climbing down the chimney?"

He made a face.

I added, "I mean the little ones. You know they're not all big."

He reminded me of what the fireplace looked like when we first bought the house. It was full of burnt ashes and debris so thick that it was hard to clean out the bottom. The fire screen was torn, and the safety glass doors were broken. The cement bottom and the side block walls were also cracked and discolored black.

We talked about the chimney sweep we hired to clean the flue and how he was astonished by what he found. He discovered the chimney cap was off, and the flue was blocked from top to bottom. It took him all day to clean it. When he finally finished, he told us it was the worst he had ever cleaned. He was surprised no one died in the house after lighting a fire. He then asked us what we were burning. We told him we had just bought the house and had no clue what the previous owners had burned. He also couldn't imagine the temperatures needed to crack the bottom and sides of the fireplace.

I told Dean, "Do you ever wonder how much evidence of the creatures we threw out? The house probably had tons of DNA evidence: hair, fingerprints, and other things. Maybe even a bone or two. After all, they were burning something in the fireplace and the oven. As far as we know, there could be lots of hair and DNA evidence still on the roof, considering the creature is sitting there."

He replied, "Yes I've thought about it. I've also thought about all the stuff I found buried in the yard. Remember it took me months to dig it out and get rid of it. Some of it was really bizarre."

I shook my head and stated, "We sure messed up. We should have never bought this house. What a nightmare."

15
Fighting Destiny

Forest pathway before sunset

Over the next few months, the creatures could have done anything they wanted. Our attention was elsewhere. My father suddenly became ill with terminal cancer and passed away. It was the worst thing that could have happened, and my world collapsed. I can't even express the pain of missing him; I won't even attempt.

~~~

By the end of June 2015, I was feeling lost and disconnected. I asked Dean to bring home our household belongings. Most of our stuff had been in storage for over a year and a half. We packed the garage and rented a storage unit when we first discovered Bigfoot. We wanted to make room in the garage to park both cars inside for security reasons. It also cleared the driveway for Adam's truck.

Months later, we rented more storage units and packed most of our household belongings when we decided to sell the house. The house inside was perfectly staged for prospective buyers but felt stripped and cold. All our family memories were packed. We had yet to determine if or when we would sell the house. All our attempts had failed. Dean could see I was struggling to move forward, so he brought home most of our belongings. He emptied out three of our four storage facilities.

Having our stuff again made me feel better, like welcoming a long-lost friend home. It reminded me of our good times as a family with dreams and goals. Before our nightmare began, and took them away. Our lives had changed so drastically. None of us could have ever imagined being in such a doomed situation. As I unpacked our belongings, I looked at a picture of myself as a little girl and thought about our current situation.

Most women would understand. I couldn't be alone in my home; someone always had to be with me. Having Bigfoot watching 24 hours a day was like being pursued by the ultimate stalker. I depended on the men, dogs, and guns to protect me.

Sadly, we had adjusted to our new way of living under threat. So far, our house rules have been working. This was the retirement we had worked so hard for and planned so carefully. Although, I lived every day trying to figure out a way to get out without destroying what was left of our family or ruining our children's future. Losing our home and becoming a financial burden at our age terrified me. I guess I had learned there were worse things in life that could happen.

On the other hand, I may have given up. I didn't have the

strength to keep fighting a destiny that already seemed determined. I believed everything happened for a reason, and for some reason, all this was happening to us. I reminded myself that the world was full of tremendous pain and suffering, and we just had to deal with creatures. It didn't even compare to the anguish of a loss.

Nevertheless, we lived in a dangerous situation and needed to stay diligent and aware of our surroundings. Many things were happening in the neighborhood, and I was tired of keeping it a secret. I thought about our next-door neighbors, Mike and Carla, and figured it was time they knew about everything, including the books I had written.

I called Carla, and we talked for more than an hour. It felt good to talk to her again. Mike and Carla already knew about Bigfoot in the woods. They had spoken to Mr. Hill during the investigation and had their own experiences, which I wrote about on the first night I saw the Bigfoot.

I informed Carla about other incidents we had with the creatures. She said she knew we were having problems with Bigfoot. They, too, had been outside at night with flashlights more than a few times after hearing strange noises. We talked about many things, but I was surprised when she told me something about our neighborhood that I didn't know.

She asked if I had seen the ghost of a woman walking up and down the street at night. She figured we would have captured footage of the spirit with our many cameras. I told her no, but a strange woman that looked like a ghost often walked up and down the street early in the evening. She had long, dark hair and was very thin and pale looking. We used to see her walking around but hadn't seen her lately. Carla had seen her too and agreed she was strange. We both wondered where she came from, but we didn't know.

I described the other ghosts we had seen and the ones we captured on video. We talked about Adam, and I told her what had happened to him. She was very concerned and said she would give him a unique charm to carry on him for protection. I thanked her, and then we talked about Steve and Becky.

Steve and Becky were the young couple with fraternal twins who lived next door to the forest. I had informed Becky last year about the creatures peeking through their windows, and I hadn't spoken to her since. Steve and Becky had abruptly moved. Carla didn't know what happened, only that Steve walked outside, placed a "for sale" sign in their yard, and left. Their house was vacant and for sale. Carla was bewildered; it happened so fast, and they never mentioned they were moving. They had been close neighbors and talked frequently. She found it strange that she didn't even know where they had gone.

I told Carla about my conversation with Becky and about the Dog-man beasts. I reassured her that I hadn't seen the beasts in over a year. When I saw them, I explained that some abandoned mines were closed a few miles away. Evidently, the local mining company was collapsing the mines and burying them. Mr. Hill had recently informed me that the land had been leased to another mining company. I thought the Dog-man beasts came from the mines, and maybe they returned from where they came. It seemed logical to both of us, but it was just speculation.

Before our conversation ended, I informed Carla about the books I had written and that I had kept the forest location a secret. She agreed that keeping it a secret was a good idea. She also didn't want the neighborhood turned into a circus. I offered her copies of my books and gave her the website's name. She said she would tell Mike, and he would pick up the books later. She had to go, and we hung up.

~~~

On July 5, Mike called while William and I talked in the kitchen. Mike asked if he could stop by to pick up the books and tell me something. Minutes later, he arrived and asked if I was recording audio on July 4. I told him no, the fireworks were too loud, and I didn't want to record the creatures anymore. He said, "Well, it was hollering last night really loud."

Mike couldn't believe how loud the creature was; he was stunned. He described the sound and attempted to mimic it. From what he explained, the Bigfoot hollering was similar to the one we heard on October 13, 2012, when it all began. William and I just listened as Mike started to explain what had happened.

Mike said, "It was a little after midnight, and something hit the side of the house. It sounded like a loud bang! I grabbed my gun and a flashlight and went outside to see what it was."

He told us that he looked at the side of his house and perimeter but didn't see anything. He started to walk in the street, heading towards the forest path, when he heard the creature. He said, "It went off hollering the most incredible howl! It was so loud it vibrated my chest. I listened to it, hoping you were recording audio. It hollered for a few minutes and then suddenly stopped."

Mike wanted to find the creature and see if it would howl again. So he cautiously went into the forest and sat by the creek to listen. He said, "It was completely quiet."

He remained by the creek for a few minutes and then left. He wanted to go back into the forest again, another night, to look for Bigfoot. I explained why doing that would be dangerous. I said, "The creatures are not at all what you think."

I handed my books to him and said, "Promise me you will read the books first. Then if you still want to sit in the forest, let me know. I will turn on the audio, give you the night vision scope, and be ready to call 911. I can't stop you, but you need to read the books first."

We talked a little longer, and I showed him some evidence we had collected. He promised that he would read the books by the time he left.

After Mike left, I thought about his false impression of the creatures and their origin. Initially, we had the same belief that Bigfoot were just an undocumented species, a prehistoric undiscovered apelike beast, and finding one would be a big deal. We were so naïve that we even sought evidence of them. However, they were not at all what they were perceived to be. They were something else.

Why did we have a false impression? Due to our limited understanding of these creatures, they exist and flourish. In fact, I believe they depended on our superior thinking. They show themselves to us as simple beast to give that impression. They allowed us to see what they wanted. If you think about it, considering our advanced technology, finding a large creature in a forest shouldn't be that hard. How could an eight-foot or ten-foot-tall creature stay hidden? Or disappear before your very eyes? Mike believed he was alone in the forest, but I guarantee he was not. The beast was watching him after it summoned him into the woods. What happened to Mike was also disturbingly familiar, except this time, he was outside with a flashlight and a gun searching for them.

I also noticed the mesmerizing look in Mike's eyes as he described the beast hollering. He recalled a compelling sound he couldn't help but follow just as we did. I believe most people would search for the creatures after hearing one.

I wanted Mike to read my books first to spare him from repeating our mistakes. The creatures were vengeful beasts, and if bothered, they would retaliate. I hoped that my writings would serve as a warning.

A few days later, when Mike didn't return, I called Carla to ask her what Mike had decided to do. She said she didn't know. He was busy working and hadn't read the books yet.

~~~

With that issue optimistically postponed, I wanted to stay busy too. So for the next several weeks, I focused on redoing all the curtains in the house. Even though we already had curtains and blinds, they just didn't seem thick enough. I wanted to triple the curtains so no light showed through at night.

After doing radio, I got a lot of email advice, and someone wrote me that the creatures could track our whereabouts in the house due to the lighting. The lights would change every time we went in and out of a room. I didn't know if that was true, but it made some sense. The last thing I wanted to do was make it easier for the creatures to watch us.

With my sewing machine unpacked from storage, I began sewing new curtains. I had several sets to do, and sewing always made me feel better. It was good therapy, and the new curtains could help shield us from the creatures. Or so I believed.

~~~

On August 10, at 9:50 p.m., I cleaned the kitchen. Our sons had helped, and the only thing left to do was the dishes. William and Adam went upstairs, and Jack went into the laundry room to start a load of laundry. The laundry room was located just off the kitchen down a short hallway. Dean was upstairs with Rocky and Heidi, putting away clean clothes. I asked Jack to bring me a clean dishcloth from the laundry room. He walked into the kitchen, and I met him halfway. He gave me the cloth and returned to doing his laundry.

I went to the kitchen sink and started wetting the cloth when suddenly I heard a growl. I froze, holding the dishcloth under the water, and listened. The growl was louder than the water running down the sink through the dishes. It was long, deep, and threatening. My eyes rose, and I immediately looked at the window above the sink; the growling was coming from the window.

I stared at the curtains, and that's when it dawned on me; they were just fabric used to cover a blind and a window. The kitchen window was the last curtain I did the day before. I slammed the water handle off, cursed, and jumped away from the sink. My skin started crawling, and my heart was racing. I freaked out and bolted into the laundry room. Jack immediately knew something was wrong the second I flew into the room. I had my hand over my mouth to silence my screaming, and I was jumping around.

He said, "I heard you yell, what's wrong?"

It took me a few seconds to explain what happened.

He said, "Calm down, maybe when you turned on the water there was something in the sink, or the dogs made a sound."

"No that's not what happened!" I replied as I shook my head. "The growl was coming from the window. It was growling at me!"

Jack went into the kitchen to check it out, while I peeked into the kitchen from the hallway to watch. He first looked for the dogs. They were not around. He walked over to the sink to see if something in it could have made the sound. He tried a few things hoping to replicate it, from the water running down the sink to the garbage disposal turning on and off. He also checked to see if the dishwasher was operating. The dishwasher was off; I never started it. I said, "None of those sounds even come close. It was growling from the window!"

He pulled back the curtains and opened the blinds to look out the window. I cringed, but he didn't see anything other than his reflection. He went into the dining room, grabbed a flashlight, and headed toward the backdoor.

I panicked and said, "What are you doing?"

Jack pulled back the curtains covering the backdoor, peeked through the window panes, and quickly opened it. The motion-sensor light above the door was already activated. He stepped outside and shot the flashlight around the yard. He focused on the darkest areas beyond the porch light.

At the same time, Dean returned from upstairs with Rocky and Heidi. When Rocky and Heidi saw the backdoor open, they quickly ran through the kitchen and out the door. Jack stepped back inside and said, "There's nothing by the window."

Dean asked what happened, and we explained.

Later that evening, as Dean and I sat in the office, I was still upset. It really bothered me that, for whatever reason, I thought the curtains would provide protection. Somehow, when I tripled the curtains, it made me feel more secure. "Why did I think that?"

The creature caught me completely off-guard. I told Dean, "You know, it was probably growling to let me know, that despite blackening out the curtains, we can't hide from them."

What was I thinking? I wasn't thinking at all, and a week later, my lack of judgment caught up with me.

16
Don't Go Upstairs

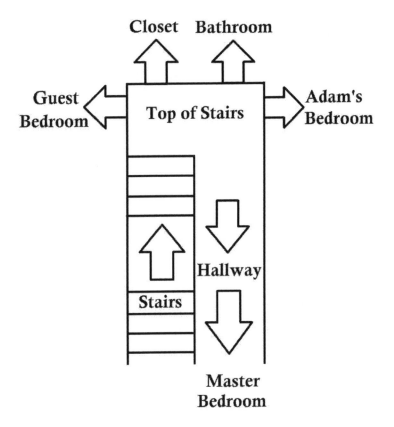

Map of front staircase and hallway

On August 18, Dean made an early dinner, and after we ate, I fell asleep on the couch in the family room. I woke up a few hours later. It was around 9:30 p.m. I headed for the office but heard Dean on the phone; he was talking to his friend, Jim. Not wanting to listen to his conversation, I went into the kitchen to clean it.

I cleaned the kitchen and placed the dishes in the sink, but there was no way I would do them. I was afraid to stand in front of the kitchen window at night. Dean had told me he would do the dishes or one of our sons would. After I finished, I quietly went into the office to check my email and work on a few things. Dean was still talking on the phone at his desk.

I checked my email and tried to concentrate on working, but something was bothering me. I could hear Adam's heavy footsteps upstairs. His footsteps were echoing above the office, along the edge of the ceiling. Adam's bedroom sat directly above the office, but it was unusual to hear his footsteps. I also heard other weird sounds of movement that I didn't normally hear. I looked at the cameras and noticed Adam's truck wasn't in the driveway. I interrupted Dean's conversation and asked, "Adam's not home?"

He said, "I know."

Bewildered, I said, "Well, I just heard footsteps walking along the edge of the ceiling."

I pointed my finger at the ceiling area where I heard the footsteps. I said, "If the footsteps aren't coming from Adam or his room, then they're coming from the front porch roof. A creature is walking on the roof."

Dean quickly told Jim what was happening and then got off the phone and grabbed his gun. He wanted to go outside and check. "No, please don't go outside." I pleaded.

The thought of Dean going outside to confront Bigfoot again scared me. I said, "The creature is probably going up the roof to a higher level or getting down. I don't want you in danger anymore. As long as it stays away from the doors, we'll just monitor it. When Adam gets home, then all of you can go outside and check."

He looked at me and reluctantly agreed. Dean knew I was fragile and couldn't take another loss in the family. I was worried about him. He left the office and took his gun to check all the doors entering the house. He wanted to make sure they were locked. A little frustrated that I didn't want him outside, he went to the kitchen and started washing the piled dishes in the sink.

A few minutes later, Rocky ran from the family room through the kitchen barking. He stopped in the foyer below the staircase. He barked again, growled, and raised his head to sniff up in the air, looking confused. Dean quickly followed him to check the front door. I was sitting at the desk in the office, watching Rocky and the cameras. I yelled to Dean, "It's okay. I don't see anything on the cameras or by the front door. Rocky hears the creature on the roof; that's why he's confused and barking."

Rocky stayed in the foyer, whimpering and growling with his hackles raised. Dean wanted to go outside again, but I said, "No, I don't want you in danger anymore."

I explained that after losing my dad, I didn't want to lose him as well. He understood and went back into the kitchen while I talked to Rocky. I whispered, "Rocky, it's upstairs," as I pointed up, "It's on the roof, I heard it too."

I got up and tiptoed to the bottom of the staircase. I petted Rocky and whispered, "Let's go upstairs and see where it is. Come on, let's go upstairs."

I called Rocky several times as I quietly snuck up the dark staircase. But he refused to follow. He just sat and watched me go up. At the time, I thought it was a little strange; he usually raced everyone to the top of the stairs the second he saw a foot on the staircase.

It was very dark and quiet when I reached the top. All the room doors that connected to the upstairs hallway were closed. There were four rooms connected to the upstairs hallway: a bathroom, a guest bedroom, Adam's bedroom, and the Master bedroom.

Jack and William were also upstairs but on the other side of the house. The other side of the house had another staircase and hallway. You had to go through the guest bedroom upstairs to get from one side to the other. The guest bedroom had a door on the far side of it. Due to the guest bedroom separating the hallways, I couldn't hear them; likewise, they couldn't hear me.

Upstairs, alone in the dark, I decided to listen to the walls. I wanted to track which way the creature was traveling. I figured it was just outside Adam's room, so I first decided to listen through his bedroom door. I tried to sneak up on it, but the floor squeaked as I stepped forward. I stopped for a few seconds and then continued.

With my right arm to my side, I put my left ear, shoulder, and arm against his door. I leaned into the door as quietly as possible, pressing my body against it. It was so dark that I could barely see the master bedroom door in front of me at the other end of the hallway.

I listened for a few seconds and heard air moving through his room. I figured it was the central air conditioner since the sound was a calming pattern. I closed my eyes to concentrate on listening. And moments later, "Bam!-bam!" A painful pounding slammed against my eardrum from the other side of the door. My eyes opened, my heart jumped, and my neck twisted in a jerking movement. My mind signaled, get away from the door! It's standing on the other side of it!

The door was struck twice rapidly from the other side, directly against my ear. Whatever *"it"* was, it was behind the door, hiding in Adam's room. It knew I was on the other side of the door listening and didn't want me listening to it. Immediately I realized I was in danger. I was alone in the hallway, and no one in the house knew I was there.

Run before it opens the door and grabs you! My instincts kicked in. I looked at the staircase but don't recall going down it. However, I do remember thinking; *will I make it to the bottom of the stairs?*

I was running, screaming, crying, and shaking when Dean flew around the corner from the kitchen and grabbed me. He had no clue what had happened. He found me in the dining room, so hysterical that I could barely speak. I kept repeating, "Bam, bam!" and motioning, something hitting my ear. He held me up as I collapsed in his arms. I was so distraught that I was unable to form a coherent sentence. Something was hiding in Adam's room, and I was the only one who knew it.

Dean was frantic and kept asking, "What's wrong?! What happened?! What's the matter?!" as he held me tightly.

Not getting any answers, he finally held me up with one arm and pulled out a dining room chair. He sat me in the chair and said, "What happened?!"

Feeling faint, I gasped for air and finally pointed upstairs and mumbled, "Somethings in Adam's room. I went upstairs."

He quickly explained that he needed to leave me for a few seconds and told me not to move. He ran to the back staircase and yelled for Jack and William. The next thing I knew, Jack was standing next to me, trying to calm me down and figure out what had happened.

Dean and William quickly armed themselves and ran upstairs to Adam's room. They positioned themselves in the hallway as William cautiously listened through the door first. Dean tried to open the door, but it was locked. He needed the key. They yelled down the stairs, "Where's the key?!"

All our sons lock their doors due to the dogs being able to open them. Jack calmly asked me, "Where's the key?"

But I couldn't remember. I couldn't think! Jack kept saying, "Focus on the key, where is it?"

Dean and William were about to break through Adam's door when I finally remembered where I had hidden the key. Jack yelled to them, "Wait!"

Jack ran into the office to get the key and then flew upstairs with it. Outside of Adam's bedroom, Rocky and Heidi were also in the hallway, agitated due to all the commotion.

Dean unlocked the door, flung it open, and rushed in with William. Rocky and Heidi followed. They searched Adam's room and closet but found nothing.

Adam's bedroom was calm and quiet, although one of his windows was unlocked. He had the vent to his portable room air conditioner placed out the window. Sometimes our sons used portable air conditioners to further lower their room temperature.

Dean pulled the vent out of the window and locked it. He called Adam to tell him to come home immediately, and then he and William searched the entire house.

Jack stayed with me in the dining room, trying to provide comfort. I was crying uncontrollably.

When Dean and William returned, I was finally able to explain to all of them what had happened. Jack asked me to reenact the incident. I didn't want to, but he suggested that air pressure could have caused the knocking sound. He said, "The central air conditioner kicking on and off could have moved the door, and it just sounded like knocking."

Jack was trying to suggest possibilities to calm me down. I said, "No, that's not what happened. It wasn't a knocking sound. That thing hit me from the other side of the door. It did it twice, directly on my ear, and it did it on purpose. It knew - I was there!"

I continued to cry. William handed me tissues as he sat across the table, thinking. He said, "I was just in that hallway about thirty minutes before dad got us. I was getting some stuff out of the bathroom. I came through the spare bedroom and didn't turn on the hallway light. As I crossed the top of the stairs, I got a strange feeling. Like someone wanted to throw me down the staircase. It was a strange thought, and I just ignored it. It's never happened before, and I don't have those types of thoughts. I went into the bathroom, got my stuff, and left."

I blew my nose and wiped my puffy eyes. I was terrified!

After listening to William, Jack remembered something. He said, "It's probably a ghost."

Jack mentioned that when he ran into the office to get the key, the cameras went off, but before he left the room to run upstairs, the cameras went on again. Something created a power surge to occur. That's why he suspected it was a ghost.

William, Jack, and I stayed in the dining room. While Dean rechecked the house until Adam came home.

When Adam arrived, we told him what had happened. Jack asked Adam if his door moving could have made the knocking sound. Adam said his door, when closed, doesn't move, so it could not have been the door making the sound.

After I calmed down, we all went upstairs to reenact the incident. Adam was right; regardless of the air, his door didn't move. They even tried reopening the window and putting the vent back. But still, when closed, his bedroom door had no play in it.

They all agreed it was probably a ghost, but I thought otherwise. I heard its heavy footsteps, and Rocky heard and smelled it too. Does that seem like a ghost? I wondered.

With no reasonable explanation for what happened, I begged Adam not to stay in his room. I kept telling him something was in there. He asked if it was a Bigfoot. I replied, "I don't know what those creatures can do?! But whatever it was? I heard it walking, and so did Rocky. Something went into your room and left. Please stay in the guest bedroom or downstairs."

Adam replied, "For how long, Mom, one day, two days, or a week?! How long, do you want me to stay out of my room?!"

I started crying again and said, "I don't know, I don't know, but there was something in there!"

He said, "Yeah, but there's nothing we can do about it! We don't even know what it was."

Adam sounded stressed and frustrated by the situation. Dean told Adam to calm down.

Adam said, "I'm tired and I'm going to bed."

He stayed in his room despite my warnings. I, on the other hand, refused to go upstairs anymore alone. Never again, I said.

Logically I had no one to blame but myself for what happened. I was the one who wanted to sneak up on it. Whatever *"it"* was? After seeing the things I had seen, I should have known better. Never confront anything alone. I felt like an idiot acting in a B-horror movie that goes looking for a creature and gets eaten.

17
The Surrender

Camera that moved mounted on fence

Still terrified, I kept thinking that somehow a creature got into the house due to the heavy footsteps I heard. However, as Jack mentioned, it could have been a ghost due to the camera screens in the office turning on and off. Either way, we needed a camera to cover the front porch roof and the windows outside Adam's Bedroom.

I told Dean we'll just have to figure out a way to do it. We had tried in the past, but the motion sensor lights of the porch, when activated on high, would cast a bright glow on the camera screen. The bright glow would make the camera useless.

I thought, maybe a long-range camera would work? We purchased additional cameras and requested overnight shipping. We also bought another microphone.

In the meantime, I convinced Adam to sleep downstairs in the office until we could set up the new cameras. He agreed so I wouldn't worry. I was concerned that a creature would sneak through his windows at night.

When the new cameras arrived, we installed the long-range camera thirty feet from the house and tilted it upward. Fortunately, it worked despite the porch lights. After setting up the additional cameras, Adam checked the recording system to ensure it worked.

I repositioned all the cameras the next day, especially the one shooting across the front porch. I wanted the camera to cover more of the corner next to the front porch windows.

~~~

A few nights later, on August 22, I walked into the office and noticed that the camera shooting across the front porch had changed. It wasn't covering the corner anymore. It was back to where it used to be, further out. I asked Dean if he had moved the camera, and he said, "No."

Somebody moved the camera, *I thought.* The camera had three screws holding its position, so it couldn't move without someone unscrewing them. Since the camera was recording, I checked the footage to see exactly when it moved.

It moved Saturday morning at 9:07, and everyone in the house was asleep. On the recorded footage, the camera moved on its own; smoothly back to its original position. It was strange; since no person was captured on the video that could have moved it. *And what happened to the screws? Who unscrewed them? (**Moving camera**)*

I immediately checked all the other cameras that were recording around the house. On the other recorded cameras, no one approached, walked, or drove by the house the entire morning. Outside, it was calm and quiet, although one of the cameras that should have recorded behind the camera that moved didn't record. It was the only camera out of eight hooked up to the recording system that malfunctioned. It stopped recording for 15 minutes. It recorded video before the camera moved and after, but not during.

The camera that moved was on the fence next to the front door. *(See chapter photo)* The camera that didn't record was also on the fence but, on the other side, pointed at the pool. Therefore, I could assume that whatever moved the camera came from the other side of the fence. Whatever *"it"* was, it disrupted the camera that should have captured it, but what about the screws?

~~~

The following morning, I went outside to readjust the camera, and I couldn't move it. I had to unscrew it. Also, turning it was not smooth or easy; it was jerky and stiff, nothing like the movement in the video.

When I asked Adam to recheck the recording device, he said the camera behind the fence should have worked. There was no technical reason it didn't. It was bewildering.

~~~

Over the next few weeks, the camera held its position, and they all recorded. The system was working fine, and I spent nights watching the camera focused on the front porch roof outside Adam's windows. I feared the creatures' return. I was so afraid that I stayed on the bottom floor of the house. I would never go upstairs alone again, regardless of what I heard. I figured it was only a matter of time before something else happened, and a few weeks later, it did.

~~~

On Sunday, September 13, Adam made a snack and was eating at the kitchen island. It was early evening, and Dean and I were watching television in the family room. The dogs were with us, sleeping nearby. When Adam finished eating, he went up the front staircase to his room. A few minutes later, we heard him banging on William's bedroom door. Adam was upstairs in the back hallway, and he sounded upset. The back staircase carried the sound into the family room. I muted the television, and Dean and I listened.

We heard Adam shouting to William through his bedroom door. Adam asked William, "Did you bang on my bedroom door and try to open it?"

Seconds later, William opened his door and quietly talked to Adam. Jack was in the shower; we could hear the water running. A minute later, we heard Adam knocking on the bathroom door to ask Jack the same question.

I yelled upstairs to Adam, "What's wrong?!"

Adam came running down the backstairs into the family room and franticly asked, "Where are the dogs?"

He quickly came around the couch and saw the dogs sleeping in the room. He plopped down in the chair across from me. He looked panicked and out of breath. He said, "I'm freaked out."

Dean and I waited for him to catch his breath to explain.

Adam said, "I just went upstairs to my room. No one was following me or in the hallway. I went into my room locked the door, turned, took two steps towards my desk, and someone started banging on my door, trying to turn the door handle to get into my room. I turned around and quickly opened the door to see who it was, but no one was there. I ran to the other side of the house hoping it was William or Jack that banged on my door. It wasn't them, William was in his room working on his computer, and Jack was taking a shower."

Adam paused for a few seconds. He was thinking of something and said, "Really, there wasn't enough time for anyone to get out of the hallway without me seeing them. Although all the doors upstairs were open, I just don't' think there was enough time."

I said, "I told you something was upstairs. At least we now know it's probably a ghost and not some creature coming through your window. I don't even want to tell you what kind of creature I suspected. Put it this way, just the thought gave me nightmares."

"It sure sounds like a ghost," Dean said, and Adam agreed.

"No," I said, "It's not just a ghost; we have a bigger problem! It can bang on doors and move door handles. Which means it's dangerous! It can hurt us anytime it wants to, and it's probably what's been scratching you. Whatever it is, it comes and goes. I've realized that sometimes the dogs won't go upstairs. They used to sleep in the spare bedroom during the day, but not anymore.

Dean said sarcastically, "Just great, another problem."

"What are we going to do?" I asked.

Then, I realized we were talking about a ghost, which meant we couldn't see it. I whispered to Adam, "Go upstairs and tell your brothers there's a ghost in the house and you cannot stay in your room. I don't even know if we should be talking about it. It could be listening to us!"

Dean and Adam informed William and Jack and then checked all the rooms in the house but found nothing. Also, the cameras captured nothing outside approaching the house.

~~~

Adam stayed downstairs for a few days while Dean and I emailed people asking for help. After doing the radio interviews, I was in contact with people who knew about these things. After we found out what to do, we contacted a priest to bless the house. When the priest arrived, we told him what had happened, and he knew what to do. Evidently he had dealt with this type of problem before. We also did other things to protect ourselves, hoping they would work.

However, despite our decisive actions, I feared going upstairs alone. Especially since we didn't know what type of ghost was in the house or how long it's been inside? The priest said it might take a few blessings before all the activity stopped. Nevertheless, we did whatever we could to eradicate it.

~~~

A few days after the blessing, Adam came home at 10:31 p.m. As usual, he backed his truck into the driveway. I watched on the cameras as he parked, got out, and slowly headed toward the house. I noticed something was wrong; Adam paused, stopped, and looked around. He also had what appeared to be his gun out. I yelled for Dean to go outside, but he was busy in the kitchen. Dean met Adam at the front door and asked if he was okay. Adam said yes and then walked into the office.

I asked, "Why did you pull your gun out and look around?"

He replied, "A Bigfoot was growling at me. I first heard it after I got out of my truck and opened the backdoor to get my stuff out. That's why I stopped and listened. I looked at the forest and it growled again. That's when I knew it was a Bigfoot. It was a deep guttural growl. I felt it go through my chest. I pulled out my gun and started to walk towards the house and that's when I heard it again. I stopped on the porch to look around because I couldn't tell which direction it was coming from."

I said, "Yes, that sounds like it was a Bigfoot growling. Their growl is like that, it resonates. I watched you get out of the truck and you were no threat, yet it threatened you. I bet it doesn't like the new cameras or the new motion sensor alarms we placed around the perimeter. Your dad and I installed them today. They beep whenever someone approaches within fifty feet of the house. Needless to say, the alarms have been beeping since the sun set."

I explained to him how the alarm system worked. He agreed that adding the system was a good idea, but he didn't like coming home and being growled at.

The alarms outside kept beeping as the days passed, but my attention was elsewhere. I was busy listening for any suspicious sounds inside the house; I feared walking around, even on the bottom floor. I left most of the lights on at night and the ones illuminating the stairwells. I found myself repeatedly peeking up the stairs, listening, and praying. I was praying that nothing would manifest. Everyone in the house was diligent as we waited to see if anything else strange would happen, and a month later, it did. But it wasn't at all what we expected.

~~~

The ghostly activity at Adam's job returned with a vengeance. He came home and explained. Again, he was working alone in the building late at night. He was sitting at his desk when suddenly, a dark entity snuck up behind him. He could feel it and see its dark reflection on his computer screens. He was afraid to turn around.

Adam said, "The feeling of terror went through my body. I sat facing my computer, pretending to type. I had an overwhelming feeling; not to turn around. Actually, it was an understanding like something very bad would happen if I did. I didn't even have a fight-or-flight response. It was a feeling of complete surrender."

The entity stood behind him, watching the back of his head for about a minute, and then vanished as quickly as it appeared. He said, "I could feel it when it left. The whole atmosphere in the room changed."

It scared him half to death. He was stressed and distraught. He firmly believed the entity had been following him.

He explained that one night when he and Amanda were dating, he picked her up after work and went to the walking bridge by the river. The bridge was a scenic place where families went at night to walk. They had just arrived at the bridge and parked when suddenly Amanda started screaming and swatting at something that wasn't there.

He said, "She jumped out of the truck and started to run. I had to catch her to find out what happened. She was crying and shaking. She said something in the truck was pulling her hair, touching, and scratching her. She even showed me some scratches."

At the time, he didn't know what happened and thought she did it for attention. He said, "Well, I didn't see anything!"

He convinced Amanda to get back into the truck and took her home. He also mentioned other incidents involving the truck, but mainly with the radio; evidently, sometimes, it turned on while he was driving. He insisted he never touched it.

We told Adam it sure sounded like an entity was following him. Dean and I felt helpless and horrified. We didn't know what to do other than listen. Adam stated, "I'm done with it! I'm not working late again, which means my projects aren't going to get done. I will probably get fired if I don't find another job."

Dean and I understood and stated we would support him. His company had recently transferred ownership, and he wasn't happy anyway. So we figured, why take any chances? In the meantime, I gave Adam some holy crosses to carry in his truck.

The next day, Adam started looking for a new job, and a few weeks later, his supervisor, Ryan, approached him and asked if they could talk after hours. Adam figured Ryan found out he was planning on quitting. After their meeting, Adam came home and spoke to me in the office. He said, "Guess what else showed up during my meeting with Ryan?

I asked, "What?"

He said, "Ryan waited around until everyone in the building left, and then he came to my cubical to talk. He asked me a whole bunch of questions. I was answering all his questions, when the entity started typing. It sounded like it was typing on a computer keyboard on the other side of the room. Ryan interrupted me and said, 'Do you hear that? We are the only ones in the building.' I didn't answer him I just kept talking. I wanted to get out of there!

The entity continued typing until Ryan finally jumped up and said, 'don't you hear someone typing?!' I said, 'Yes! The building is haunted.'"

He said Ryan looked at him and then went to the area where he heard the sounds. He looked around for a few seconds. Finding nothing and now spooked, he returned and told Adam, "There's nothing in that cubical, not even a keyboard."

At that moment, I interrupted Adam and asked, "The entity was making a typing sound? I have the chills just thinking about it! I didn't tell you, but one night a few months ago, I set a recording device in the office. It only recorded for forty minutes because the batteries died. I placed the device on the desk by my computer. I was typing on the computer and your dad was watching television in the family room. He called me to watch something and I left the room. You can even hear us on the recording talking in the family room. But on the audio recording it sounded like someone was typing in the office when nobody was there. It was bizarre. Your dad and I compared the sound to our computer keyboards but it didn't match."

"Do you still have the recording?" Adam asked.

I replied, "I think so."

"Let me listen to it," he said.

After listening to the recording, he said, "Yes, that sounds like a mechanical keyboard and you guys have membrane keyboards. That's why the sounds didn't match; they're different keyboards."

He crossed his arms, leaned back in the chair, and said, "That's disturbing."

"Why?" I asked.

He replied, "When the entity was making the typing sound at work, it sounded like a mechanical keyboard too. I am the only one that I know of at work that has a mechanical keyboard. It was mimicking me typing."

I said, "You mean it was making that sound? That means it was here in the office watching me. It was following you!"

Video Moving camera

18
Grim Reality

Eight cameras on one TV screen recorded

Two cameras not recorded but with microphones

Some type of entity attached to Adam was following him. At least, that's what we determined. Really, it was the most likely answer to explain the recent ghostly activity. Either it followed him home from his haunted work building, or it was already present roaming through the neighborhood when it attached.

Over the years, I have seen other ghostly things in the forest. Therefore, it could have been one of them. Our new night vision cameras captured a glowing image suddenly appearing and jumping into the woods, although it looked like solid energy with no actual shape. *(Ghost flash)*

It had also crossed my mind, because of the footsteps I heard and the strange behavior of the creatures, that it could have been some kind of cloaking related to them. After all, we didn't know everything about the beasts, and we knew little about the entity. I guess anything was possible, but we chose the most likely.

After contacting people who knew about ghostly attachments, we took their advice. It was unknown territory, and they warned that paranormal activity could increase. Realizing Adam was in the most danger, we purchased additional religious charms for him to carry. We also placed crosses that had been blessed over our entrance doorways to prevent it from reentering the house.

Adam no longer worked late or alone in the haunted building. He had done a few job interviews that appeared promising. As for us, we haven't had any additional ghostly activity inside the house since the blessing, but only time would tell if it was over.

Still, I was fearful. Fearful that it could still be lurking, I refuse to go upstairs alone. The last thing I wanted to see was a ghost appearing in the hallway or behind me in the bathroom mirror, especially any of the entities Adam described. I considered placing recording devices inside the house to see if they would record any ghostly activity. I considered it but didn't do it because I didn't want to listen to the recordings. I wondered what if I heard something I wish I hadn't. I had already heard sounds so chilling that I regretted hearing them. Did I really want to hear more creepy voices and sounds inside the house? The answer was "No."

It was easier to believe it was over, even though it may not be true. We had already recorded creatures we knew nothing about, which became a nightmare. Only a fool would travel down the same path twice, knowing it only leads to more horror and fear. I already suffered from horrible nightmares, and so did Adam and Jack. *Why add to them?*

After all, we still had Bigfoot in the neighborhood and, so far, managed to avoid any deadly confrontations. It took effort and many cameras and alarms to set up a perimeter that seemed to be working. The creatures stayed away from the cameras. At least that's what we determined to be a fact. Also I considered the Bigfoot and Dog-man the same related species. They were both creatures of questionable origin. The Bigfoot, as currently known, wasn't some type of ape or so-called missing link. The truth would be found somewhere between what some believed were inter-dimensional beings while others insisted were demons. They were absolutely creatures that even I couldn't fully comprehend. I knew they were physical beings to a degree, but they did the strangest things. I would describe it as supernatural.

They defied logic and physics in how they moved to avoid the cameras. Their ability to hide was also remarkable. They could reshape the forest and blend into various backgrounds as if they commanded the elements of Mother Nature and perception.

It was baffling that my handheld camera couldn't capture clear video of them. Also, the creatures seemed to know things they shouldn't. They knew every time the camera was pointed at them, no matter how many ways I tried to hide the camera's lens. Within seconds, they would shake the forest, and a strange wind would appear. Now, I only attempt to capture video, standing at least five feet from the window and shooting through it. However, the minute the forest starts to shake, I stop. Why risk angering them?

In addition to the Bigfoot, I also see what appears to be another type of creature that is small and black. It sometimes travels with them, maybe to assist with something. I don't know what they are since they also don't video clearly.

~~~

I once questioned why someone who studied Bigfoot wouldn't jump at the chance to trade places with us. They could have bought our house and studied them for as long as they wanted. However, after years of observation, I think I know the answer. Anyone who really knows anything about them knows better than to deal with these beings. No one that has seen what I have seen would want to live across the street from them. Although I could be wrong, the option would always exist since the creatures would never leave, according to Mr. Hill.

He recently wrote on a popular Bigfoot forum under his real investigator name. The Bigfoot would always be across the street from our house, as they had been for generations. The creek and the forest were part of their territory. He is a well-known, highly respected senior investigator who documented these creatures. He is also a brave man to have spent over thirty years pursuing these bizarre beasts.

In the end, despite every terrifying encounter due to my writing and collecting evidence, I am content knowing that our story has been documented no matter what happens to us. People will read about these creatures and learn from our mistakes and observations.

I write to families in similar situations to warn them. Like us, they live under siege, locking their doors and securing their windows at night. They stay inside no matter what they hear after the sun sets. Sadly, families live in dangerous situations, thinking no one would believe them. I encourage them to come forward and tell their stories.

Our situation is dangerous, even though some would say, "So far, the entity hasn't hurt you, just like the Bigfoot hasn't." Despite all the horrifying events I documented. Events where many times we could have simply disappeared, but didn't due to our diligence?

Therefore the real question should be - why have we survived? In reality, protecting ourselves against these creatures was impossible based on their capabilities. Do we continue to exist as long as they deem necessary, for whatever reason? Do they also suffer from conflict, some that would do away with us and others that stop them? Either way, we were going to remain diligent until we could move.

~~~

In the meantime, Dean sits in the office looking at homes for sale. He optimistically predicts that the housing market should improve in early 2016. He figures with the market up, we would have a good chance of selling our house and buying a new one.

According to him, 2016 would be the year we could escape. It was good news, but what about my conscience? Should we tell the new buyers what happened to us?

Dean suggested we wait and see who offers to buy the house, and then we'll cross that bridge. He said, "Who knows, maybe they won't believe in Bigfoot or the supernatural, and we could sell the house to them."

That's what I called wishful thinking. Just as I had wished we'd sold our house to a Bigfoot organization or someone interested in studying these creatures, we could have sold with a clear conscience.

As we wait for something good to happen. I sit in the office, watching the cameras, viewing video recordings, and listening for strange sounds inside and outside the house. I also hope to listen to all the recorded audio on the devices in the drawer.

At this time, I don't plan to write any more books about our situation. It's a good thing to have nothing more to write. It means our security is holding, although it's nighttime again, and the motion sensor alarms keep beeping. But on the cameras, we see nothing, even though it is a little unnerving, especially since they are motion sensor alarms. They have been beeping since the day we installed them. However, I believe; that we only need to be worried the day they stop beeping. It would mean the creatures found a way around them. Dean says, "It's not so bad listening to beeping sounds all night, considering things could always be worse."

Dean was the eternal optimist, or so I thought.

Videos Ghost flash
Bigfoot or Dog-man Peeking

BIGFOOT NIGHTS
A true story

Visit my website or YouTube channel for additional sound and videos of the creatures.

Website: (100BigfootNights.com)
YouTube Channel: (100BigfootNights)

Made in the USA
Las Vegas, NV
02 September 2023

76960081R00081